TREASURE CHEST
For English Language Learners

Practice Book
Annotated Teacher's Edition
Vocabulary Blackline Masters

Macmillan McGraw-Hill

Introduction

The ELL Practice Book is designed to give English Language Learners practice with the skills taught throughout each unit. The practice pages cover the following domains in grades 1–6:

- Reading Comprehension Strategies and Skills
- Phonics Strategies
- Vocabulary Strategies
- Language Structure
- Writing skills
- Oral Language Development

Practice Pages

The practice pages for each unit allow children to practice the skills for that week. Students will complete a vocabulary page, a phonics page, a comprehension page, and a language structure page for each week.

Additional Pages in the Teacher's Annotated Edition of the Practice Book

This annotated teacher's edition of the Practice Book contains two additional elements:

Activity Pages

These activity pages suggest several games and activities the students can engage in with their individual sets of vocabulary cards.

Vocabulary Black Line Masters

Each of the thirty weeks of the series is assigned three pages of BLMs containing vocabulary cards for the students to cut out. The first page contains the words for the beginning leveled reader for that week. (All students in the class are responsible for learning the beginning level words.) The second page contains the words for the intermediate level, and the third page contains the words for the advanced level (including any overlapping words from lower levels.) Copy the number of pages you need for the students in each reading group, and distribute these as handouts.

Contents

Vocabulary BLMs

Name _____

Vocabulary: Dictionary/Unfamiliar Words
Look up these words in the dictionary.
Then write the letter to match each word to its meaning.

1. ___d___ solve   **a.** something that is hard to understand

2. ___c___ clues   **b.** proof

3. ___b___ evidence   **c.** hints

4. ___a___ mystery   **d.** find the answer

5. ___h___ creativity   **e.** taking what does not belong to you

6. ___g___ planned   **f.** someone an item belongs to

7. ___e___ stealing   **g.** thought ahead about what to do

8. ___f___ owner   **h.** imagination

Choose four vocabulary words from above.
Write a sentence using each word.

Example: How the snake got out of its cage is a mystery.

Answers will vary.

9. _____

10. _____

11. _____

12. _____

Name _____

Phonics: Words with Short Vowels

• The words *ad, bell, band, dock,* and *mug* have short vowel sounds.

ad   bell   band   dock   mug

Circle and write the word in each group that has a short vowel sound.

1. (land)   bake   lane   _____land_____

2. kite   ice   (ball)   _____ball_____

3. cake   (dog)   toe   _____dog_____

4. (leg)   bowl   grape   _____leg_____

5. case   (sock)   road   _____sock_____

6. (pen)   room   bear   _____pen_____

Write four sentences using words that have a short vowel sound.

Answers will vary.

7. _____

8. _____

9. _____

10. _____

Comprehension: Problem and Solution

Think about the problems and solutions in *The Mystery of the Lost Glasses.* Write a response on the lines.

1. What is the main problem in the story?

   Brett needs to find the owner of the glasses

   he found.

2. What clues did Brett use to solve the mystery?

   The glasses case had words on it.

3. How did Brett's father help him solve the mystery?

   He suggested that Brett put an ad in

   the newspaper.

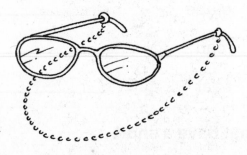 

4. Why was Brett afraid to pick up the lost glasses?

   He didn't want anyone to think he'd stolen them.

5. How did Dr. Alan help Brett find evidence about the owner?

   He looked at his records for a patient with

   those initials.

Language Structure: Sentences

Read the different types of sentences below. Write *D* if the sentence is declarative. Write *C* if the sentence is a command. Write *E* if the sentence is an exclamation. Write *Q* if the sentence is a question.

1. ___D___ I found a pair of glasses.

2. ___Q___ Who could they belong to?

3. ___C___ Please call me.

4. ___E___ Happy Birthday!

5. ___Q___ Can I help you?

6. ___C___ Watch your step.

Write one sentence for each sentence type.

Answers will vary.

7. _____

8. _____

9. _____

10. _____

Name _____

Vocabulary: Context Clues/Surrounding words

- **Context clues** are words in a sentence that help you learn the meaning of a word you don't know.

On the lines below, write the context clues that can help you figure out the meaning of the underlined word.

1. Over many years, a plant or animal's body makes <u>adaptations</u> to fit the climate where it lives.

   _____fit, where it lives_____

2. Even though the desert has hot, sunny, and dry weather, many plants and animals have found ways to survive this <u>climate</u>.

   _____hot, sunny, and dry weather_____

3. It's not easy for people to <u>survive</u> in a desert, but some animals and plants are able to stay alive.

   _____stay alive_____

4. During the summer, the <u>temperature</u> in the desert can get hotter than 100°F.

   _____summer, hotter, 100 °F._____

Write your own sentence using one of the underlined words from above.

5. _____Answers will vary._____

Name _____

Phonics: Words with Long *a*

• The words *rain, cake,* and *tray* have the long *a* sound.

rain   cake   tray

Circle the words with a long *a* sound and write them on the lines.

1.	(crate)	palm	food	_____ crate
2.	land	(bake)	ant	_____ bake
3.	dust	leak	(pain)	_____ pain
4.	body	(day)	fur	_____ day
5.	(grape)	dune	wild	_____ grape
6.	silk	(wait)	cow	_____ wait
7.	(gain)	coin	van	_____ gain
8.	show	mask	(page)	_____ page

Write two sentences using words that have the long *a* sound.

Answers will vary.

9. _____

10. _____

© Macmillan/McGraw-Hill

Name _____

Comprehension: Main Idea and Details

- A **main idea** tells the most important idea about a topic.
- **Details** give more information about it.

Read the main ideas below. Then, write one detail for each main idea, using information from the story.

1. **Main Idea:** Deserts are dry, and rain is scarce there.

   Detail: ___The temperature in the summer can be_____

   _____more than 100°F._____

2. **Main Idea:** The prickly pear cactus is a desert plant.

   Detail: ___It grew very quickly in Australia and_____

   _____spread everywhere._____

3. **Main Idea:** The bilby is an animal that survives well in the desert.

   Detail: ___It has long ears like a rabbit, is active at_____

   _____night, and lives under the dirt during the day.___

4. **Main Idea:** The honey-pot ant survives well in the desert.

   Detail: ___It can store food in its body and save it for_____

   _____when there is no food._____

5. **Main Idea:** The galah is a bird that survives well in the desert.

   Detail: ___It can escape the heat by flying._____

   _____

© Macmillan/McGraw-Hill

Name _____

Language Structure: Subjects and Predicates
- The **subject** of a sentence tells what the sentence is about.
- The **predicate** tells what the subject does or is.

Underline the subject of each sentence.
Circle the predicate.

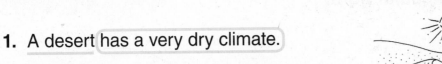

1. A desert has a very dry climate.

2. Rocks and sand are in the desert.

3. The Great Sandy is a desert.

4. The Great Sandy is one of Australia's biggest deserts.

5. The Great Sandy has many red sand dunes.

6. Grasses and trees grow in the Great Sandy Desert, too.

7. The desert is a very difficult place to live in.

8. Brian and Maria have always wanted to see desert animals.

9. The cactus survives in the dry climate.

Write three sentences. Underline the subject and circle the predicate in each sentence.

Answers will vary.

10. _____

11. _____

12. _____

© Macmillan/McGraw-Hill

Vocabulary: Word Parts/Compound Words

• We make **compound words** when we add two words together to make one new word.

The words below are compound words. Write the two words that make up each compound word.

1. wildlife   wild + life
2. sometimes   some + times
3. moonlight   moon + light
4. basketball   basket + ball
5. lunchroom   lunch + room
6. waterfalls   water + falls
7. birdcage   bird + cage
8. airplane   air + plane
9. steamboat   steam + boat
10. shoelace   shoe + lace

Think of two more compound words. Write sentences with these words.

Answers will vary.

11. _____

12. _____

Name _____

Phonics: Words with Long *e*
 • The words *feet* and *tea* have the long *e* sound.

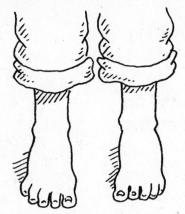

feet   **tea**

Circle the word in each group with a long e sound.

1.	neat	den	pack	neat
2.	dam	home	tree	tree
3.	safe	beat	lake	beat
4.	green	frog	hunt	green
5.	say	car	deep	deep
6.	sheep	back	fan	sheep
7.	dime	leaf	wall	leaf
8.	try	more	free	free

Write two sentences using words with the long e sound.

Answers will vary.

9. _____

10. _____

Name _____

Comprehension: Main Idea and Details

- A **main idea** tells the most important information about a topic.
- **Details** add support to the main idea by telling more about it.

Match the main idea on the left with its detail on the right. Write the letter of the main idea on the line. The first one has been done for you.

Main Idea

a. Isle Royale is a good place for wildlife.

b. Wolves travel in a group called a pack.

c. Moose are large and heavy animals.

d. Loons are birds that are afraid of people.

e. Newts are amphibians.

f. Foxes live in the woods in small families.

g. Beavers build dams in the marshes.

Detail

1. __a__ People are not allowed to hunt in Isle Royale, so the animals are protected.

2. __d__ If a person goes too close to a loon's nest, the bird may leave its nest behind.

3. __f__ Foxes hunt hares that live in the woods.

4. __c__ Scientists think that the moose probably swam to the island because they are too heavy to walk on ice.

5. __b__ Each wolf pack hunts for prey together.

6. __g__ Beavers use twigs and branches to stop the water from flowing. This forms a pond.

7. __e__ Newts start life in the water as as tadpoles. They move to the land when they grow up.

Language Structure: Simple and Compound Sentences

- **Compound sentences** are two simple sentences connected with a comma and the conjunction *and*, *but*, or *or*.

Underline the two simple sentences.
Circle the conjunction that joins them.
Then write it on the line.

1. ____*or*____ Visitors can fly to Isle Royale National Park, (or) they can sail.

2. ____*and*____ We visited the park, (and) we saw many birds.

3. ____*and*____ There are many different species of plants, (and) there are many animals too.

4. ____*and*____ People can hike (and) they can swim at Isle Royale.

5. ____*but*____ We wanted to take pictures of the animals, (but) we forgot our camera.

6. ____*or*____ Wild animals must be protected, (or) they will die.

7. ____*but*____ Wolves hunt moose, (but) they also hunt smaller animals like rabbits.

Write three compound sentences using *and*, *but*, or *or*.

Answers will vary.

8. _____

9. _____

10. _____

Name _____

Vocabulary: Dictionary/Pronunciation and Meaning

- The **dictionary** tells you how many syllables, or parts, there are in a word.

Use a dictionary to find the pronunciation and meaning of the following words. Then rewrite the word with a line between each syllable.

1. apartment _____a/part/ment_____

2. elevator _____el/e/va/tor_____

3. intruder _____in/trud/er_____

4. strange _____strange_____

5. astronaut _____as/tro/naut_____

6. guards _____guards_____

7. machines _____ma/chines_____

8. cool _____cool_____

9. uniform _____u/ni/form_____

10. trouble _____trou/ble_____

Choose two words from above and use them in sentences.

Example: Jessica rode the elevator to the top of the building.

Answers will vary.

11. _____

12. _____

Name _____

Phonics: Words with Long *i*

• The words *kite*, *light*, *fly*, and *pie* all have the long *i* sound.

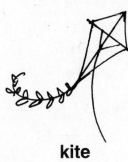

| kite | light | fly | pie |

Read each word. Write the word in each group with the long *i* sound.

1.	(bike)	eight	six	_bike_
2.	lake	(sight)	lit	_sight_
3.	choice	(sky)	rake	_sky_
4.	finger	toad	(lie)	_lie_
5.	(nine)	none	screw	_nine_
6.	frog	bake	(shy)	_shy_
7.	(cry)	free	tame	_cry_
8.	clock	(might)	cane	_might_

Write two sentences using words with the long *i* sound.

Answers will vary.

9. _____

10. _____

Name _____

Comprehension: Analyze Character

Think about the characters, or people, in *Elevator to Trouble.* Read the sentences below. Write the name of the character each sentence describes.

1. Very strange things happened after this boy rode an elevator to see his friend Anton.

   _____ Chris _____

2. She let Chris go by himself, after he promised to call her.

   _____ Mom _____

3. They wore strange clothes and drank some juice in the lunchroom.

   _____ The man and woman _____

4. He felt really proud going to his friend's apartment alone.

   _____ Chris _____

5. He drank something that looked like juice, and wondered who the intruder might be.

   _____ The man _____

6. She didn't really want her son to go to Anton's apartment alone.

   _____ Mom _____

Chris was scared when he was hiding in the lunchroom. Write a sentence about his feelings.

Example: Chris was nervous.

7. _____ Answers will vary. _____

Language Structure: Complex Sentences

- A **complex sentence** has two or more related ideas. These ideas are joined by conjunctions such as *after, although, as, because, before, if, since, unless, until,* or *when*.

Underline each idea in the sentences below.
Circle the conjunction that joins them.

1. She wanted to talk to her friend (before) she started the project.

2. She finished her project (although) it was difficult.

3. Chris won't visit Anton (unless) Anton is home.

4. Chris couldn't move (because) he was so scared.

5. Chris saw that there was no handle (when) he looked at the door.

6. Chris called his Mom (after) Captain Ruiz gave Chris the phone.

7. They left to play outside (after) they finished dinner.

8. I hid underneath the bed (when) she told a scary story.

9. Jana walked quickly (although) we walked very slowly.

10. Mark was in trouble (because) he tried to scare Lynn.

Write three sentences using different conjunctions from above.

Answers will vary.

11. _____

12. _____

13. _____

Name _____

Vocabulary: Context Clues/Paragraph Clues

Read the paragraphs below. Use the context clues in each paragraph to help you understand the meaning of the underlined words. Then, explain their meaning in your own words.

Peter's aunt drives an <u>ambulance</u>, or a van that is used to move sick or injured people from one place to another. She shows Peter how to wrap wounds with a <u>bandage</u>, or a strip of gauze that protects injuries. He is happy to learn about first aid. He will know how to help when someone is hurt.

1. ambulance _van that is used to move sick or injured people from one place to another_

2. bandage _a strip of gauze that protects injuries_

Carla and May buckled their life vests and started paddling. They rode in a <u>raft</u>, or small rubber boat, as it rushed down the swift river. The river <u>slithered</u> and curved smoothly down the hillside, like a snake. This was the most exciting part of their Girl <u>Scout</u> troop's camping trip. As the raft went over a big rock, water soaked the girls. When they finished, they felt very proud and brave.

3. raft _a little boat_

4. slithered _curved smoothly, like a snake_

5. scout _a group of people enjoying outside adventures_

Write two sentences using two underlined words from above.

Answers will vary.

6. _____

7. _____

Name _____

Phonics: Words with Long *o*

• The words *stone, oak, snow,* and *post* all have the long *o* sound.

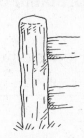

stone   **oak**   **snow**   **post**

Read each word. Circle the word in each group with the long *o* sound.

1.	ten	flower	(bone)	_____ bone
2.	dot	(goal)	book	_____ goal
3.	clock	foot	(glow)	_____ glow
4.	(roam)	stir	top	_____ roam
5.	kite	guard	(show)	_____ show
6.	door	(cone)	lake	_____ cone

Pick four words with the long *o* sound from above. Write a sentence using each word.

Answers will vary.

7. _____

8. _____

9. _____

10. _____

Name _____

Comprehension: Analyze Character, Setting, and Plot
Answer the following questions about the characters, setting, and problem of *The Secret Code*.

1. How did Kathryn feel when she found Uncle Abe's book?

   She was curious and wanted to learn the code.

2. Describe how Kathryn feels about her aunt and uncle.

   She likes to be with them. They are her favorite

   people in the world.

3. How did Uncle Abe and Kathryn describe the desert?

   It is hot, sunny, and dry with lots of sand and a few

   cactuses.

4. What did Kathryn do when the snake bit Uncle Abe?

   She went home to find help.

EHT RETTEL
SI NETTIRW
NI EDOC

5. Why did Kathryn leave Uncle Abe in the desert?

   He needed to stay very still because of his

   snake bite.

Name _____

Language Structure: Run-on Sentences

- A **run-on sentence** joins two or more sentences that should be written separately.

Write *R* if the sentence is a run-on sentence. Write *C* if the sentence is a complete sentence.

1. They are planning a party it is for Peter's birthday. __R__

2. She could not break the code alone, so she asked for help. __C__

3. There is a secret way of writing things Kathryn wants to learn about it. __R__

4. Since they were in the desert, it was often hot and dry. __C__

5. The book was on the table she thinks something is in it. __R__

6. Kathryn found the secret book and discovered the secret. __C__

7. Uncle Abe and Kathryn went exploring Aunt Rita did not come. __R__

8. She felt proud the code made more sense. __R__

Rewrite the run-on sentences above. Make each one into two separate sentences.

9. They are planning a party. It is for Peter's birthday.

10. There is a secret way of writing things. Kathryn wants to learn about it.

11. The book was on the table. She thinks something is in it.

12. Uncle Abe and Kathryn went exploring. Aunt Rita did not come.

13. She felt proud. The code made more sense.

Vocabulary: Context Clues/Descriptions

- **Context clues** are other words in a sentence that can help you learn a word's meaning.

Use the context clues in each sentence below to help choose the best word to complete the sentence.

athlete	heroine	medal
competed	exercises	training

1. If you want to be a great _____athlete_____, you need exercise, rest, and healthy food.

2. In the movie, the _____heroine_____ was so brave, honest, and smart.

3. The ice skaters did their very best in the competition, trying to win the gold _____medal_____.

4. The baseball team arrived early to do their warm-up _____exercises_____.

5. Tracy stretched her muscles before she _____competed_____ in the race.

6. James goes to bed early and eats healthy food when he is _____training_____ for a race.

Write sentences using two of the words in the box.
Example: A good athlete can run fast.

7. _____Answers will vary._____

8. _____

Name _____

Phonics: Words with *ch* and *tch*

- The words *chain, pitcher,* and *arch* all have the ch sound at the beginning, middle, or end.

chain   pitcher   arch

Write whether the *ch* sound is at the beginning, middle, or end of the word.

1. chase ___beginning___

2. ketchup ___middle___

3. latch ___end___

4. chip ___beginning___

5. hatch ___end___

6. catcher ___middle___

7. chair ___beginning___

Think of two words with the *ch* sound. Use those words to write a sentence.

8. ___Answers will vary.___

_____

© Macmillan/McGraw-Hill

Name _____

Comprehension: Author's Purpose

- An author may write to **inform, persuade,** or **entertain.**

Answer each question using what you know from the book.

1. Why do you think the author wrote that the crowd was cheering for Wilma?

   The author wanted to show that they were excited

   about Wilma's race.

2. Why do you think the author wrote that when Wilma was a child, her doctors said she'd never walk?

   The author wanted to show how amazing it was

   for Wilma to run in a race.

3. Why do you think the author wrote about how Wilma's track team lost a competition?

   The author wanted to show how Wilma never gave

   up, but trained harder.

4. Why do you think the author wrote a story about Wilma Rudolph?

   To show that people can win in life even if they

   have a hard time at first.

Name _____

Language Structure: Common and Proper Nouns

- A **common noun** names a person, place, thing, or idea.
- A **proper noun** is capitalized and names a particular person, place, thing, or idea.

Read the word. Tell if the noun is a common noun or a proper noun.

1. athlete _____common_____

2. Wilma _____proper_____

3. basketball _____common_____

4. medal _____common_____

5. Rome _____proper_____

6. Olympics _____proper_____

Write two sentences using a common noun. Underline the common noun.

7. _____Answers will vary._____

8. _____

Write two sentences using a proper noun. Underline the proper noun.

9. _____Answers will vary._____

10. _____

Name _____

Vocabulary: Dictionary/Word Origins

- Many English words come from other languages. A word's **origin** shows which language first used the word.

Use a dictionary to find the origins of these words.

WORD	ORIGIN
1. boycotts	English
2. grapes	German
3. kitchen	Middle English
4. chef	French
5. convince	Latin
6. customers	Middle English
7. restaurant	French
8. owners	Middle English
9. business	Middle English

Write some English words you know of that are the same in another language.

Answers will vary.

_____

_____

Name _____

Phonics: Words with /th/, /sh/, /wh/, and /ph/

- The words *thirty, shed, whisk,* and *phone* have consonant diagraphs *th, sh, wh,* and *ph*.

<u>th</u>irty   <u>sh</u>ed   <u>wh</u>isk   <u>ph</u>one

Circle the consonant diagraphs in the following words:

1. ship   6. southern

2. wash   7. alphabet

3. shine   8. photo

4. thing   9. whole

5. ethnic   10. what

Think of two words with a consonant diagraph and use each of them in a sentence.

Answers will vary.

11. _____

12. _____

Name _____

Comprehension: Make Inferences

- When you read, you use what you already know to understand what you are reading. This is called making an **inference**.

Read the details from *Lili Kiat*. Then, choose the inference that makes sense.

1. Lili goes to the store to buy vegetables for her family's restaurant.

    a. Lili likes to go shopping.

    b. Lili's family trusts her to help them with their business.

2. Lili decided not to buy the grapes on her shopping list.

    a. She didn't like the taste of grapes.

    b. She wanted to help the farm workers.

3. Some important customers ordered a dish called The Treasure Boat.

    a. It was the restaurant's most famous and tasty dish.

    b. They really like boats and wanted to play with it.

4. The farm workers hope for people to support the boycott.

    a. They want to receive fair wages and good treatment.

    b. They don't like grapes and don't like to work.

Read the following sentence and write your own inference.

5. Mary bought flour, sugar, butter, eggs, and cocoa powder at the store. She greased and floured a big pan, and heated the oven.

    What is Mary doing?_____

    Mary is baking a cake.

Language Structure: Singular and Plural Nouns

- A **singular noun** names one person, place, thing, or idea.
- A **plural noun** names more than one. Most plural nouns are formed by adding *s* or *es*.
- When a noun ends in a consonant and *y*, the plural is formed by changing the *y* to an *i* and adding *es*.

Write the plural form of each noun.

1. branch   branches
2. grocery   groceries
3. citizen   citizens
4. restaurant   restaurants
5. city   cities
6. wish   wishes
7. berry   berries

Choose two singular words from above.
Write a sentence for each.

Answers will vary.

8. _____

9. _____

Choose two plural words from above. Write a sentence for each.

9. _____

10. _____

Name _____

Vocabulary: Word Parts/Plural Endings

- Most words become plural by adding an *s*.
- If the word ends in an *s* or a *ch*, add *es* to make it plural.
- If the word ends in *y*, change the *y* to an *i* and add *es*.

Make the words plural.

1. grass   grasses
2. danger   dangers
3. panda   pandas
4. country   countries
5. habitat   habitats
6. study   studies
7. treasure   treasures
8. region   regions

Write three sentences using plural words from above.

Example: Many different animals live in forests.

Answers will vary.

9. _____

10. _____

11. _____

Phonics: Complex Consonant Clusters

• The words *shred, throat, sprang, script, stream,* and *splash*
begin with consonant clusters *shr, thr, spr, scr, str, spl.*

shred

throat

sprang

splash

script

stream

Circle the word in each group that begins with a consonant cluster.

1.	shrimp	shirt	shark	shrimp
2.	think	threw	zoo	threw
3.	speak	sprout	spoon	sprout
4.	strong	forest	clown	strong
5.	tree	cry	split	split

**Pick a word with a consonant cluster from above. Write a
sentence using the word.**

6. _____ Answers will vary. _____

Name _____

Comprehension: Fact and Opinion

• A **fact** is a statement that can be proven.
• An **opinion** is what someone thinks or believes.

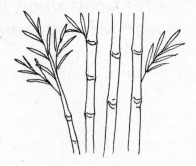

Read the sentences below. Write F if the statement tells a fact. Write O if the statement tells an opinion.

1. ____O____ Pandas are the cutest animals in the world.

2. ____F____ Bamboo is one of the only foods pandas will eat.

3. ____F____ Bamboo is a type of grass that grows over 100 feet high.

4. ____O____ Everyone should like to eat bamboo because it is delicious.

5. ____O____ Pandas look like they are friendly.

6. ____F____ It is cold and rainy on the mountains where bamboo grows.

7. ____F____ There are very few pandas living in the wild.

8. ____O____ When a panda honks and cries, it sounds scary.

Write two of your own opinions about pandas.

9. _____ Answer will vary. _____

10. _____

© Macmillan/McGraw-Hill

Language Structure: Irregular Plural Nouns

- Some nouns have special plural forms, such as *man, men*.
  Some nouns have the same singular and plural forms, such
  as *sheep*.

Write the plural form of each noun.

1. Some pandas eat (bamboo). _____bamboo_____

2. Giant pandas live in bamboo (forest). _____forests_____

3. Pandas' (tooth) are flat. _____teeth_____

4. China had many (dynasty). _____dynasties_____

The words below are singular. Write the plural form of the words below.

5. leaf _____leaves_____

6. sheep _____sheep_____

7. tree _____trees_____

Write sentences using the singular form of the words above.

Answer will vary.

8. _____

9. _____

10. _____

Name _____

Vocabulary: Dictionary/Idioms

- **Idioms** are phrases, or groups of words.
- Together, the words in an idiom mean something different than each word means by itself.

The idiom *lend a hand* means "to help out."
Use the idiom *lend a hand* in a sentence.

Example: Chris likes to lend a hand in the kitchen.

1. Answers will vary. _____

Find the word *hand* in the dictionary and write the definition.

2. Possible answer: an appendage used for grasping and holding. _____

The idiom *give her a hand* means "to applaud." Use the idiom in a sentence.

3. Answers will vary. _____

The idiom *talking your ear off* means "to talk a lot." Use the idiom *talking your ear off* in a sentence.

4. Answers will vary. _____

The idiom *keeping me hopping* means "keeping me busy." Use the idiom in a sentence.

5. Answers will vary. _____

Find the word *hopping* in the dictionary and write the definition.

6. Possible answer: propelling oneself by springing forward on one foot _____

Name _____

Phonics: Words with *ô* and *ä*

- The words *door, cord, shark,* and *dart* make the sound *ô* and *ä*. The *ô* sound is made in the words *door* and *cord*. The *ä* sound is made in the words *shark* and *dart*. Each of these words is an *r*-controlled word.

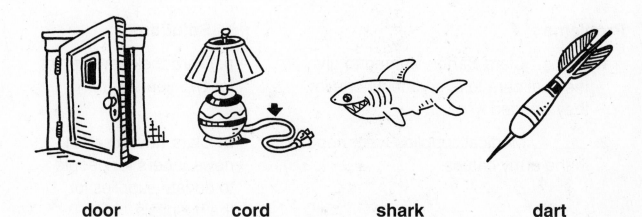

| door | cord | shark | dart |

Look for the *r*-controlled words and write them down.

1. mouse   (lord)   project   _____ lord
2. (farm)   frame   fairy   _____ farm
3. (part)   frown   one   _____ part
4. plane   ring   (floor)   _____ floor
5. town   (army)   group   _____ army
6. (sore)   found   close   _____ sore

Write two more *r*-controlled *ô* and *ä* words.

Answers will vary.

7. _____

8. _____

Comprehension: Problem and Solution

Read the sentences that tell about Clara Barton's problems and the solutions that worked. Match each problem to its solution.

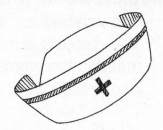

Problems

1. ___f___ Clara Barton wanted to give medical care to everyone whenever they needed it.

2. ___e___ Medical supplies were needed in the army camps.

3. ___b___ Civil War hospitals did not have the supplies, food, and water they needed.

4. ___a___ Clara's brother got hurt in an accident.

5. ___d___ Soldiers who were wounded in the Civil War did not have enough doctors to take care of them.

6. ___c___ Some of the soldiers died alone, far from their families.

Solutions

a. Clara took care of him for two years.

b. Clara advertised in newspapers for people to donate supplies for the hospitals.

c. Clara Barton read to the soldiers or just sat with them so they would not be alone.

d. Clara Barton worked very hard day and night to help the doctors take care of them.

e. Clara Barton drove the supplies on wagons to get them to the army camps.

f. She formed a group of volunteers that would give medical care to everyone. It was called the American Red Cross.

Name _____

Language Structure: Possessive Nouns

- A **possessive noun** is a noun that shows who or what owns or has something.
- A plural possessive noun is a plural noun that shows who or what owns or has something. When a plural noun ends in *s,* add an apostrophe (') to make it plural possessive.

Write each phrase using a possessive noun.

1. the volunteers of the army   the army's volunteers
   _____

2. the nurses of the hospital   the hospital's nurses
   _____

3. the ideas of the people   the people's ideas
   _____

4. the lights of the town   the town's lights
   _____

5. the desk of Clara Barton   Clara Barton's desk
   _____

6. the notebook of Thomas   Thomas' notebook
   _____

7. the medicine of the patient   the patient's medicine
   _____

8. the beds of the soldiers   the soldiers' beds.
   _____

Write the possessive form of the word in parentheses.

9. _____Barton's_____ work created the idea of the Red Cross. (Barton)

10. Other _____people's_____ ideas also helped make groups that gave medical care. (people)

11. _____America's_____ history is very interesting. (America)

Name _____

Vocabulary: Word Parts/Base Word

- A **base word** is the main part of a word. For example, the base word of *eaten* is *eat.* The base word can help you understand a word's meaning.

Underline the base words. Then write a sentence for each word.

Example: Have you eaten today?

Answers will vary.

1. marshes _____

2. molting _____

3. poisonous _____

4. slithered _____

5. rainy _____

6. forests _____

7. harmless _____

8. threatened _____

9. dangerous _____

10. swampy _____

11. injection _____

12. predatorial _____

Name _____

Phonics: Words with *âr* and *î*

- The words *stair, snare, pear,* and *where* all have different spellings, but the ending sounds are the same, or rhyme. These words make the *âr* and *î* sounds.

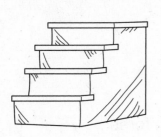

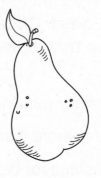

| stair | snare | pear | where |

Circle all the words that rhyme in each group.

1. (dare) tar more (fair)

2. peer (chair) (tear) card

3. (care) deer (hair) prey

4. (lair) (where) form rock

5. (scare) snake (bear) bore

6. far (share) deep (pair)

7. fear (hare) (there) cheer

Write a rhyme using two or more words that make the *âr* and *î* sounds.

Answers will vary.

_____

_____

© Macmillan/McGraw-Hill

Comprehension: Make Inferences

- An **inference** is an idea you get from something you read.

Read each piece of information from _Snakes in the Rain Forest._ Circle the letter of the sentence that makes the best inference.

1. The rain forest is very wet and warm.

   a. Snakes that live where it snows like to visit the rain forest.

   b. This is a good place for big snakes to live.

2. Tree snakes have colors and patterns that look like leaves.

   a. This helps them hide from animals that want to eat them.

   b. Colored snakes are prized for their beauty.

3. Snakes flick their tongues to smell the air.

   a. They like the sweet smell of the forest.

   b. They can smell their food even in the dark.

4. Some snakes have extremely poisonous venom.

   a. When they strike, their prey dies quickly.

   b. Most snakes will strike even if you leave them alone.

5. There are many layers in the rain forest.

   a. Different animals live in different layers.

   b. Snakes live only in the top layer.

6. An emerald tree boa is green. It can hide in the rain forest trees.

   a. It likes to hide because it does not like sunlight.

   b. Its color makes it easy for it to hunt for food.

Language Structure: Plurals and Possessives

- **Plural nouns** name more than one person, place, thing, or idea. They usually end in *s*.
- **Possessive nouns** show who owns or has something. They have an apostrophe (').

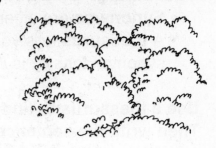

Write whether each underlined noun is plural, possessive, or both.

1. The <u>snakes</u> slithered away.

   plural _____

2. The <u>trees'</u> leaves were turning yellow.

   both _____

3. The <u>forests</u> of Central and South America are millions of years old.

   plural _____

4. The <u>Amazon's</u> animals are adapted to their environment.

   possessive _____

Write two sentences using plural nouns.

Answers will vary.

5. _____

6. _____

Write two sentences using possessive nouns.

7. _____

8. _____

Name _____

Vocabulary: Thesaurus/Synonyms

- **Synonyms** are different words that have the same meaning.
- A **thesaurus** tells you the synonym for a word. For example, a synonym for *sick* is *ill*.

Use a thesaurus to find the synonym for the underlined words. Then write the sentence again using the synonyms.

Example: Karen did not go to school because she felt <u>sick</u>.
Karen did not go to school because she felt ill.

1. Justin likes to jump out from behind bushes to <u>frighten</u> his little sister.

Justin likes to jump out from behind bushes to scare his little sister.

2. Amanda tried to <u>trick</u> her cousin into giving her the cookie.

Amanda tried to fool her cousin into giving her the cookie.

3. A family of raccoons lives in that part of the <u>woods</u>.

A family of raccoons lives in that part of the forest.

4. No matter how hard they pushed, the rock would not <u>budge</u>.

No matter how hard they pushed, the rock would not move.

5. During field day, the team that <u>tugged</u> the hardest on the rope won.

During field day, the team that pulled the hardest on the rope won.

Name _____

Phonics: Words with û

• The words *bird, Earth, person,* and *purse* have the *û* sound.

bird   **Earth**   **person**   **purse**

Read the sentences below and circle the words with the *û* sound.

1. The furry fox wakes up very hungry.

2. Everything in the forest is afraid of the serpent.

3. Most people love to learn new things.

4. He washes his shirt every week.

5. The dirt wouldn't come off the carpet.

6. Her sister won the match.

Read the incomplete words below. Add different letters to create new words. Write the new words on the lines.

7. _____ ir _____   _____ stir _____

8. _____ ear _____   _____ heard _____

9. _____ er _____   _____ alert _____

10. _____ ur _____   _____ spurt _____

Possible answers

© Macmillan/McGraw-Hill

Comprehension: Author's Purpose

- An **author's purpose** may be to inform, explain, persuade, or entertain.

Read the story details below. Place an X next to the statements that tell about the author's purpose in *The Mud Monster*.

Story Details

1. The author wrote about animals that got tricked. _____X_____

2. *The Mud Monster* teaches readers how to make mud pies. _____

3. The author wanted to teach readers not to steal from others. _____X_____

4. The author includes facts about how birds build nests. _____

5. *The Mud Monster* is a scary book. _____

6. The animals taught the fox a lesson about causing mischief. _____X_____

7. The author wanted to teach readers how to grow strawberries. _____

8. The other animals were so angry that they wanted the fox to leave the woods. _____

Name _____

Language Structure: Action Verbs

- An **action verb** is a word that expresses action. It tells what the subject does or did.

Underline the action verb in each sentence.

1. The fox <u>chuckles</u> often.

2. The rabbit <u>pushes</u> wheelbarrows full of mud from the river.

3. The raccoon <u>hurries</u> through the woods.

4. The squirrel <u>rushes</u> to the pile of nuts.

5. The blue jay <u>builds</u> a nest.

6. The chipmunk <u>looks</u> for nuts.

7. The deer <u>stomps</u> on the grass.

8. A bear <u>growls</u> at the squirrel.

9. The fox <u>hunts</u> for little bunnies.

10. The rabbit <u>follows</u> the bear into the cave.

11. The squirrel <u>swims</u> to save his spilled acorns.

12. The birds <u>fly</u> over the hungry bear.

Write three sentences using action verbs.

Answers will vary.

13. _____

14. _____

15. _____

Name _____

Vocabulary: Word Parts/Prefixes

• A **prefix** is a syllable added to the beginning of a word to change the word's meaning.

Underline the prefix in each of the words below.
Write sentences using the words.

Example: <u>re</u>heat

Dawn asked her mother to reheat her dinner.

1. <u>re</u>name   Possible answer: I renamed my doll Annie.

2. <u>un</u>kind   The bully was unkind to me.

3. <u>un</u>tie   She untied her shoelaces.

4. <u>re</u>write   Tommy has to rewrite his name.

5. <u>un</u>cover   Nancy wants to uncover a mystery.

6. <u>re</u>capture   Ben tried to recapture the butterfly.

7. <u>re</u>open   My dad wants to reopen the jar.

8. <u>un</u>married   My uncle is unmarried.

9. <u>re</u>play   I like the movie so I replay it.

Match the prefixes in the box with the words and definitions.

un	re

10. <u>re</u>do   to do again

11. <u>un</u>tie   to loosen

Name _____

Phonics: Words with Silent Letters *kn, mb, wr*

• The words *knot, climb,* and *write* have silent letters.

knot   climb   write

Match each word to its silent letters.

	Words	Silent Letters
1. _____b_____	wren	**a.** kn
2. _____c_____	tomb	**b.** wr
3. _____a_____	knife	**c.** mb

Circle the words with the silent letters in each sentence.

4. She did not know how to get to the mall.

5. Nalin couldn't figure out what was wrong with the car.

6. Rachel didn't like the lamb pattern on her skirt.

Write three sentences using words with *wr, mb,* and *kn*.

Answers will vary.

7. _____

8. _____

9. _____

Comprehension: Author's Purpose

- An **author's purpose** may be to inform, explain, persuade, or entertain.

Circle the answer that tells the author's purpose. Use what you know from *Harriet Tubman.*

1. Why did the author choose to write about how Harriet Tubman became a heroine?

    a. The author wanted to teach people about railroads.

    b. The author thought slavery was wrong.

    c. The author showed how one person can make a difference in people's lives.

2. Why did the author explain that Harriet was born a slave?

    a. The author wanted to explain why Harriet wanted to be free.

    b. The author showed how people in difficult situations can do great things.

    c. The author was trying to teach readers which states had slaves and which states were free.

3. Why did the author tell how Harriet led troops into battle?

    a. The author wanted to describe one of the jobs Harriet did.

    b. The author wanted to tell something that not many people know.

    c. The author wanted to write a war story.

© Macmillan/McGraw-Hill

Language Structure: Verb Tenses

• The **verb tense** tells when an action takes place.

Tell the tense of each underlined verb. Write *past,*
present, **or** *future.*

1. Harriet Tubman was <u>forced</u> into slavery when she was a child. ___*past*___

2. His work <u>changes</u> people's lives. ___*present*___

3. Harriet Tubman <u>helped</u> many people escape slavery. ___*past*___

4. You <u>learn</u> about interesting people in class. ___*present*___

5. People <u>worked</u> together to help others escape slavery. ___*past*___

6. You <u>will make</u> a difference in the world. ___*future*___

The sentence below is in the present tense. Rewrite the sentence in the past and future tense on the lines below.

The author writes many books about American women.

7. (past) ___*The author published many books about American women.*___

8. (future) ___*The author will publish many books about American women.*___

Write your own sentence. Underline the verb in your sentence and tell the tense of the verb.

9. ___*Answers will vary.*___

Name _____

Vocabulary: Word Parts/Inflected Verb Endings

• When you add the ending -*ed* to a verb, the word changes to past tense. For example, *walk + ed = walked*

Add the inflected ending -*ed* to each word. Remember, for verbs that end in e, drop the e and add -*ed*.

1. document + ed = _documented_

2. invent + ed = _invented_

3. interest + ed = _interested_

4. raise + ed = _raised_

5. publish + ed = _published_

6. arrange + ed = _arranged_

Write four sentences using the verbs from above.

7. _Answers will vary._ _____

8. _____

9. _____

10. _____

Name _____

Phonics: Words with Soft *c* and Soft *g* Sounds

The word *dance* has the soft c sound. The word *bridge* has the soft g sound.

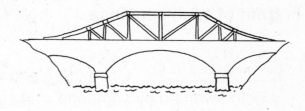

dance   bridge

Circle the word in each group with a soft c or soft g sound.

1. (circle)   cool   lap

2. good   gate   (gentle)

3. crane   (city)   cane

4. go   ghost   (generous)

5. (cinema)   crown   crop

6. good   (general)   diagram

7. (bicycle)   crib   care

8. gate   (page)   gas

Think of one word with a soft c sound and one word with a soft g sound. Write a sentence using each word.

Answers will vary.

9. _____

10. _____

Comprehension: Compare and Contrast

- When you **compare**, you tell how things are alike.
- When you **contrast**, you tell how things are different.

Read the sentences below. Write _compare_ or _contrast_ on the line in front of each sentence.

1. __compare__ Computers and skateboards were both invented by someone who wanted to make life easier and more fun.

2. __contrast__ An invention is something someone created, but a discovery is something someone found.

3. __contrast__ A spaceship is an invention, but finding a new planet is a discovery.

4. __compare__ Louis Braille and Helen Keller were both blind.

5. __contrast__ A patent is a legal document that keeps anyone from stealing an inventor's idea, but a copyright protects a writer's work.

6. __compare__ Louis Braille and Philo Farnsworth worked hard to solve their problems until they came up with new inventions.

7. __contrast__ Some inventions were made because someone wanted to create something new, but other inventions happened by accident.

© Macmillan/McGraw-Hill

Name _____

Language Structure: Main and Helping Verbs

• A **helping verb** helps the **main verb** show an action or make a statement.

Underline each helping verb. Circle each main verb.

1. She was (convinced) her son was a genius.

2. The young inventors have (worked) together.

3. They have (done) many experiments.

4. We are (trying) to create a new type of clock.

5. Mark is (inventing) all kinds of things.

6. We are (making) new things for tomorrow.

7. Rosie and Richie have (decided) to take different roads.

8. Jay was (preparing) for Franky's wedding.

9. Kaye is (trying) to fit into her dress.

10. Sara was (allowed) to go to the movies.

11. The doorman was (closing) the door.

Write three sentences using the verbs _work_, _study_, and _guide_. Use a helping verb in each sentence.

Answers will vary.

12. _____

13. _____

14. _____

Vocabulary: Dictionary/Homophones

- **Homophones** are words that sound the same, but have different meanings and different spellings. *No* and *know* are homophones.

Choose the correct homophone for each sentence. Use your dictionary to make sure your word is correct.

1. When we went on vacation, there was a pool at the _____inn_____ where we stayed. (in, inn)

2. _____Some_____ people like chocolate, but others do not. (some, sum)

3. When you get _____there_____ please call your mother. (their, there)

4. My baby brother sometimes laughs so loudly that his face is as red as a _____beet_____ (beet, beat)

Write four sentences using the words *be*, *bee*, *no*, and *know*.

Answers will vary.

5. _____

6. _____

7. _____

8. _____

Phonics: Plural Words

- When you add *-s, -es,* or *-ies* to a word, the word becomes **plural.** *Dogs, watches,* and *flies* are plural words.

dogs

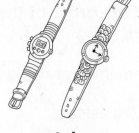

watches

flies

Read the sentences below. Circle all the plural words.

1. My dad owns many ties to match his suits.

2. Glaciers and strong winds created the South Manitou Islands.

3. We always tell stories around the campfire.

4. Many families go camping in the summer.

Rewrite the sentences. Change the underlined words to make them plural. Remember to remove the word *a* in front of plural words.

5. The teacher praised her <u>student</u>.

   The teacher praised her students.

   _____

6. Helen wanted a new <u>bracelet</u> for her mom.

   Helen wanted new bracelets for her mom.

   _____

7. A <u>puppy</u> might be a better <u>present</u> than a <u>sweater</u>.

   Puppies might be better presents than sweaters.

   _____

Comprehension: Sequence

• A **sequence** tells the order of events in a story.

Read each set of sentences below. Number each set of sentences from 1 to 4 to tell the order of the events that happened in *Ojibwe Legends*.

_____3_____ The bears all swam in a very cold lake.

_____4_____ The mother bear fell asleep.

_____2_____ The mother bear caught fish for her bear cubs.

_____1_____ Two bear cubs woke up and found their mother.

_____4_____ The animals dove into the water to find land.

_____2_____ The mother bear could not find her cubs.

_____3_____ A flood destroyed the earth.

_____1_____ The bears learned how to catch fish.

Name _____

Language Structure: Linking Verbs

- A **linking verb** links the subject of a sentence to a noun or an adjective in the predicate.

Underline each linking verb in the following sentences.

1. Wolves <u>are</u> interesting animals.

2. The young woman <u>was</u> mysterious.

3. The wolves <u>were</u> changed into people.

4. We <u>are</u> learning about Ojibwe legends in class.

5. The wolves <u>are</u> now the Quileute tribe.

6. It <u>was</u> fun to learn about the Quileute tribe.

7. The legend tells us that at one time, the Quileute people <u>were</u> wolves.

Write four sentences. Use the linking verbs from above.

Answers will vary.

8. _____

9. _____

10. _____

11. _____

© Macmillan/McGraw-Hill

Vocabulary: Dictionary/Multiple-Meaning Words

- **Multiple-meaning words** have more than one meaning.

Flood **is a multiple-meaning word. Which meaning is correct for each sentence? Write the number next to the sentence.**

flood   **1.** to overflow

2. an overflowing of water onto land

1. ___2___ It was hard for cars to drive through the flood.

2. ___1___ My mail desk was flooded with stacks of papers.

Season **is a multiple-meaning word. Which meaning is correct for each sentence? Write the number next to the sentence.**

season **1.** four periods of the year: winter, spring, summer, fall

2. to add salt or pepper to make food taste better

3. ___2___ Mom seasoned the pasta very well.

4. ___1___ Summer is my favorite season of the year.

Write two sentences each using a different meaning of the word *flood*. **Then, write two sentences using a different meaning of the word** *season*.

Answers will vary

5. _____

6. _____

7. _____

8. _____

Name _____

Phonics: Compound Words

- A word made up of two separate words is called a **compound word.** The words *fishbowl* and *bookcase* are compound words.

fishbowl

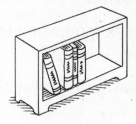

bookcase

Combine words from column A and column B to make compound words.

A	B
grand	mother
moon	flake
farm	land
snow	light

1. grand _____mother_____

2. moon _____light_____

3. farm _____land_____

4. snow _____flake_____

Choose a compound word from above. Write a sentence using the word.

5. _____Answers will vary._____

Comprehension: Summarize

Read the sentences below. Place a checkmark next to the sentences that tell important information about how hurricanes form.

a. Hurricanes form when there is warm ocean water in the air. ✓

b. Hurricane's winds can blow as fast as 200 miles per hour. _____

c. Some hurricanes cause big floods. _____

d. Hurricanes gather strength and often grow larger when they travel over water. ✓

Read the sentences below. Place a checkmark next to the sentences that tell important information about the eye of a hurricane.

a. Scientists can use a satellite to look at the eye of a hurricane ✓

b. Hurricanes can cause large waves in the ocean. _____

c. When the eye of a hurricane passes overhead, the air is very calm for a little while. ✓

d. People who live near the ocean often need to leave their homes, or evacuate, during a hurricane. _____

Name _____

Language Structure: Irregular Verbs

- An **irregular verb** is a verb that does not end in *-ed* for the past-tense form.

Rewrite each sentence by changing the verb into the past tense.

1. There is a hurricane every September.

   There was a hurricane every September.

2. The storm hits the southern part of the United States.

   The storm hit the southern part of the

   United States.

3. The wind blows very hard.

   The wind blew very hard.

4. Thousands of people are homeless.

   Thousands of people were homeless.

5. It is cloudy.

   It was cloudy.

Write a sentence in the past tense using an irregular verb.

6. _____ Answers will vary. _____

Name _____

Vocabulary: Word Parts/Prefixes

- **Prefixes** are word parts added to the beginning of another word.
  The new word has a different meaning.
  For example, *mid + morning = midmorning*

Add a prefix to each word. Check your answers in the dictionary.

re = again	**pre** = before	**post** = after	**mid** = in the middle
un = not	**mis** = wrongly	**uni** = one	**auto** = by its own power

1. __post__ war : after a war

2. __re__ washed : cleaned the dishes again

3. __pre__ test : quiz before the lesson

4. __mid__ way : halfway there

5. __auto__ mobile : car

6. __mis__ understood : not thought of correctly

7. __un__ wanted : not desirable

8. __uni__ cycle : one-wheeled bike

Write two sentences using words with prefixes from the box.

9. _____Answers will vary._____

10. _____

© Macmillan/McGraw-Hill

Name _____

Phonics: Words with Inflected Endings

The words *jumped* and *running* have inflected endings.
The inflected endings in *jumped* and *running* are made by
adding *-ed* or *-ing* to the end of each word.

jumped   running

Add *-ed* and *-ing* to each word. Write the new words on the line.

	ed	ing
1. train	trained	training
2. command	commanded	commanding
3. star	starred	starring
4. perform	performed	performing
5. act	acted	acting

Circle the form of the verb in the parentheses that best completes the sentence. Write the verb on the line.

6. Sarah is ____training____ to be a ballerina. (trained, training)

7. Teddy ____starred____ as the main dancer in *Swan Lake* last year.
(starring, starred)

8. The whole cast ____performed____ wonderfully tonight. (performed,
performing)

Name _____

Comprehension: Draw Conclusions

Match the details from *Hollywood Hounds* with the conclusions
they support.

Details

1. __a__ Dogs appear in all kinds
of movies—comedies, action-
adventures, mysteries and
even romances.

2. __d__ Some movie dogs are
pure breeds, and others are
mixed breeds.

3. __e__ Some movie dogs get
a lot of fan mail.

4. __b__ To get a dog to lick an
actor's face, the trainer may smear
ice cream on the actor's cheek.

5. __c__ Sometimes movie dogs
are discovered living in animal
shelters, where they ended up
being neglected.

Conclusions

a. Lots of people like to
watch dogs in different
kinds of movies.

b. Dogs like to lick ice
cream.

c. You may find a very
smart and well-
behaved dog living in a
shelter.

d. The breed of a dog is
not as important as
how they behave.

e. Sometimes a movie dog
is the star of the show,
and becomes even more
famous than the human
actors.

Language Structure: Pronouns and Antecedents

- **Pronouns** are words that take the place of a noun.
- **Antecedents** are nouns replaced by a pronoun.

Underline each pronoun and tell what noun it replaces.

1. Many dogs have played in movies. <u>They</u> go on the set with their trainers. ___dogs___

2. Toto was a dog who played in *The Wizard of Oz.* Everybody loved <u>him</u>. ___Toto___

3. Rosa has had her dog for many years. <u>She</u> never leaves home without her dog. ___Rosa___

4. Pal was a famous dog. <u>He</u> starred as Lassie on the television show. ___Pal___

5. Dogs have very good hearing. <u>They</u> can hear sounds that come from far away. ___Dogs___

Complete the sentences below with the correct pronoun.

6. Mia's dog rested on a mat. The dog fell asleep on ___it___.

7. Some dogs are used as guard dogs. ___They___ bark when they hear an intruder coming.

8. Charlie Chaplin had a dog named Mut. Charlie loved ___him___.

9. My grandmother is blind. ___She___ has a dog that knows how to guide people.

10. Bert lets his dogs run in the snow. He trained ___them___ to pull a sled.

Name _____

Vocabulary: Word Parts/Word Families

- Many similar words have the same base word. These words make word families.
- Some of these words are as old as the English language. They are from the same Old English word family.

Write each word next to its Old English word family.

| childish | mankind | childhood | manmade | handle |
| clothing | meaning | clothes | meanwhile | handsome |

1. child   _childish_   _childhood_

2. man   _mankind_   _manmade_

3. cloth   _clothing_   _clothes_

4. mean   _meaning_   _meanwhile_

5. hand   _handsome_   _handle_

Write three sentences using three of the words in the box.

Example: If you won't share your toys, you are being childish.

Answers will vary.

6. _____

7. _____

8. _____

Name _____

Phonics: Words that Change *y* to *i*

To add *-ed, -er, -est, -es,* and *-ly* to words ending in *y*, the letter *y* must be changed to an *i*.

marry marries married   happy happier happiest happily

Write the *-ed* and *-es* form of the base words below.

	-ed	*-es*
1. carry	carried	carries
2. study	studied	studies

Write the *-er* and *-est* form of the base words below.

	-er	*-est*
3. easy	easier	easiest
4. busy	busier	busiest

Complete the sentence below using one of the new words. Then circle the word in the sentence that ends in *-ly*.

5. The cat ____carried____ her kittens into the basket and happily
sat there for hours.

Comprehension: Draw Conclusions

- A **conclusion** should be based on the details and facts from your reading.

Match each conclusion to the fact from *Charles Drew*.

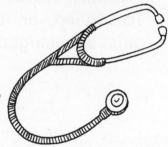

Conclusions

Facts

1. __e__ Charles' parents were very proud of him and glad he became a doctor.

a. Many medical schools turned Charles away, but he kept trying.

2. __a__ Charles never gave up his dreams.

b. Charles invented a way to separate plasma from blood. He taught other doctors how to do it too.

3. __b__ Many people's lives have been saved because of Charles Drew's work with plasma.

c. Charles knew that all blood was the same, whatever the race.

4. __c__ Charles did not judge people by their race.

d. Charles took blood donations from people in New York City and shipped the plasma to England.

5. __d__ Charles wanted to save people's lives, even if they were far away.

e. Mr. and Mrs. Drew told their children they could become whatever they wanted when they grew up if they worked hard.

© Macmillan/McGraw-Hill

Name _____

Language Structure: Types of Pronouns

- **Subject pronouns** replace the subject of a sentence.
- **Object pronouns** come after an action verb or after a word like *to, for, with, in, on, from, of, by,* or *at.*

Write whether the underlined word is a subject or object pronoun.

1. <u>He</u> discovered a way to save millions of lives.

   _____subject_____

2. Charles Drew cared about <u>them</u>. _____object_____

3. <u>He</u> wanted all people to have the chance to become doctors.

   _____subject_____

4. <u>She</u> valued hard work. _____subject_____

5. The hospital turned <u>them</u> away. _____object_____

Rewrite the sentences below. Replace the underlined words with the correct object or subject pronoun.

6. Caroline wondered about <u>her problem</u>. (it, she)

   Caroline wondered about it.
   _____

7. <u>Sara and Paul</u> tried to help. (Them, They)

   They tried to help.
   _____

8. <u>Dan</u> solved the problem by himself. (It, He)

   He solved the problem by himself.
   _____

Name _____

Vocabulary: Context Clues/Definition of a Word
Read the paragraphs. Use context clues to understand the underlined words.

When you wake up in the morning, you may not feel like you have much <u>energy</u> or strength. One way to feel more awake is to take a shower and eat some breakfast. With a microwave oven, you can <u>heat</u> up some oatmeal. Being fully awake and ready to learn before you go to school gives you a better <u>ability</u> to do well.

Match the words below to their definitions.

1. ___b___ energy   **a.** cook, or raise the temperature

2. ___a___ heat   **b.** the ability to do work

3. ___c___ ability   **c.** able to perform a task

Write a sentence using one of the underlined words.

4. _____ Answers will vary. _____

In some parts of the world, people use dried, <u>decayed</u> animal dung to cook with. They build a cooking fire by adding dung, wood, or other <u>fuel</u> to the flame. If the fire is allowed to get too hot, the cook may return to find that the meal has <u>burned</u>, and have to start over. Flames need to be tended, or fed more fuel, in order to keep burning.

5. ___c___ decayed   **a.** changed or ruined by heat

6. ___b___ fuel   **b.** anything that burns to create heat or power

7. ___a___ burned   **c.** rotten or decomposed

Write a sentence using one of the underlined words.

8. _____ Answers will vary. _____

Name _____

Phonics: Words with Long *oo* and *u* and Short *oo* and *u*

Circle the words with the long *oo* sound as in *food* or long *u* sound as in *cube*. Write them on the lines.

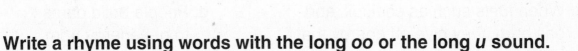

1.  (tooth)   pull   book

2.  bus   (boot)   hook

3.  (unit)   luck   shut

Circle the words with a short *oo* sound as in *book* or short *u* sound as in *fun*. Write them on the lines.

4. funnel   suit   (funnel)   tube

5. look   (look)   tooth   cute

6. hunt   (hunt)   fruit   tuba

Write a rhyme using words with the long *oo* or the long *u* sound.

Answers will vary.

_____

_____

_____

_____

Comprehension: Persuasion

• An author may use persuasion to guide readers' judgments.
**Draw a line to match each author's point from _An Eye on Energy_
with its opposing side.**

Author's Points

1. Solar power is a great alternative source of energy because it is free and safe.

2. Using water power can help us save our supplies of coal, oil, and gas.

3. Wind power is safe and free, and can make enough energy for entire cities to use.

4. When fuels such as coal, oil, and gas burn, they give off energy that creates heat or power.

Opposing Side

a. Factories that create power from wind are very noisy.

b. Cloudy and rainy days mean we cannot rely only on solar power.

c. Coal, oil, and gas are fuels that can be used up.

d. People build dams to get energy from moving water, but these dams damage the places where animals live.

Name _____

Language Structure: Pronoun-Verb Agreement

• A **present-tense verb** must agree with its subject.

Rewrite each sentence with the correct verb form.

1. Our bodies (use, uses) energy to keep us alive.
   Our bodies use energy to keep us alive.
   _____

2. We (has, have) a great need for electrical energy.
   We have a great need for electrical energy.
   _____

3. Dams help (make, makes) energy.
   Dams help make energy.
   _____

4. Everyone (is, are) able to conserve energy.
   Everyone is able to conserve energy.
   _____

5. The sun (provide, provides) energy by heating water from lakes, rivers, and oceans.
   The sun provides energy by heating water from
   _____
   lakes, rivers, and oceans.
   _____

Complete the sentences below using the correct form of the verb.

6. He ____ has ____ many friends.

7. She does not ____ have ____ a dog.

8. I ____ have ____ two brothers.

Vocabulary: Dictionary/Homographs

• A **homograph** is a word with two meanings.

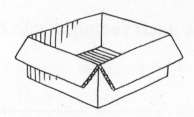

Use the homograph list to fill in the blanks. You can use a dictionary. The first one has been done for you.

just	box	present
bit	wind	content

1. When Mr. Smith was young, he used to __box__ down at the gym.

2. Mom said that dinner would be ready in __just__ a minute.

3. The teacher was surprised to see that only half of her class was __present__.

4. My dog is often __content__ to sit by my feet while I study.

5. When you wash the car, be sure to use only a little __bit__ of soap.

6. Flying a kite is fun, but if it crashes to the ground, you will have to __wind__ the string.

Write a sentence with one of the words from the box.

7. _____ Answers will vary. _____

Name _____

Phonics: Words with *oi/oy* and *ou/ow*

Circle the words with *oi* as in *moist* or *oy* as in *boy*.
Write them on the lines.

1. __joy__   cow   joy   kind

2. __toy__   toy   grind   bold

3. __foil__   sold   foil   boat

4. __coin__   chew   fine   coin

Circle the words with *ou* as in *sound* or *ow* as in cow.
Write them on the lines.

5. __hound__   hound   noise   crow

6. __town__   plus   cold   town

7. __plow__   plow   blue   road

8. __pound__   shine   pound   lawn

Choose four words from above.
Write a sentence using each word.

Answers will vary.

9. _____

10. _____

11. _____

12. _____

© Macmillan/McGraw-Hill

Name _____

Comprehension: Sequence
List the events or steps in the order they happen.

The Food Chain of the Whale

a. Plants grow on ice.

b. Whales eat krill.

c. Krill swim in the ocean.

d. Krill eat the plants.

1. _____ a _____

2. _____ d _____

3. _____ c _____

4. _____ b _____

Whales Endangered, then Protected

a. People learned to make oil, soap, and other products from whale blubber.

b. Whalers made a lot of money from selling the whales they had killed. Then they hunted more and more.

c. People passed laws against polluting the ocean and against hunting whales.

d. Lots of whales used to live in the ocean, without any danger from people.

5. _____ d _____

6. _____ a _____

7. _____ b _____

8. _____ c _____

Language Structure: Possessive Nouns and Pronouns

- A **possessive noun** is a word that shows who or what has something.
- **Possessive pronouns** take the place of possessive nouns.

Underline the possessive noun or pronoun in each sentence.

1. Spilled oil can clog a whale's blowhole.

2. A whale's pod can be made up of family or friends.

3. Their pods travel and play together.

4. Its snoring and rumbling sounds are mysterious.

5. A whale's songs can mean many things.

6. Some of their teeth are flat.

Write sentences with a possessive pronoun. Then underline the possessive pronoun.

Answers will vary.

7. _____

8. _____

9. _____

10. _____

Name _____

Vocabulary: Context Clues/Descriptions

Read each sentence below. Circle the words that help you find the meaning of the missing word. Choose the word from the word bank that best completes the sentence. Write it on the line.

creatures	defense	brittle
food chain	explorers	sleds

1. Animals, such as polar bears, whales, and penguins, live in the Arctic Ocean. They are _____creatures_____ that can survive in very cold weather.

2. Seals eat small fish. Then polar bears eat the seals. This is one example of a ___food chain___.

3. Robert Perry and Matthew Henson were famous ___explorers___. They traveled to the North Pole, a place that no one had ever been to.

4. It can be dangerous to walk on ice because it can crack into pieces very easily. Ice can be very ___brittle___.

5. Animals may have body parts that they use to protect themselves from danger. Walruses use their tusks for ___defense___.

6. Peary and Matthew needed vehicles to move themselves and their things across the snow and ice. They used ___sleds___.

Phonics: Words with *a, au, aw, alt, alk*

Read the words aloud. Listen for the sound of *a, au, aw, alt,* or *alk.* Then circle the word with that sound.

hawk

auto

1. half	(taught)	chain	*taught*
2. (salt)	dog	skate	*salt*
3. shark	(lawn)	back	*lawn*
4. meal	friend	(wall)	*wall*
5. (walk)	calf	hair	*walk*

Choose three of the circled words above. Use each in a sentence.

Answers will vary.

6. _____

7. _____

8. _____

Name _____

Comprehension: Compare and Contrast

- To **compare** means to show how things are the same.
- To **contrast** means to show how things are different.

Read the sentences below. Do they compare two similar things? Or do they contrast two different things? Write *compare* or *contrast* on the lines in front of each detail from The *Arctic Ocean*.

Main Idea   **Details**

contrast   **1.** People would be miserably cold swimming in the Arctic Ocean any time of the year. Many animals live there and feel comfortable in the cold water.

compare   **2.** During both the winter and the summer, the skies are partially dark in the Arctic.

compare   **3.** An explorer named Sir John Franklin set out to explore the Arctic in 1845. Robert Peary and Matthew Henson began a similar adventure in 1909.

compare   **4.** Under the surface of the ice in the Arctic Ocean, there are as many animals as there are in warm water coral reefs.

contrast   **5.** Fish swim by moving their tails left and right. Whales and dolphins swim by moving their tails up and down.

contrast   **6.** Many whales have a single blowhole on their backs, but one kind, called a right whale, has two blowholes.

Language Structure: Pronouns and Homophones

- Do not confuse certain possessive pronouns with their homophones, such as *their* and *they're*.

Write the pronoun that completes each sentence.

1. The first explorers to the Arctic made (they're/their)

   trip with twenty Inuit helpers. _____their_____

2. (It's/Its) very difficult to live in the Arctic. _____It's_____

3. (Your/You're) skin can freeze if (its, it's) not covered properly.
   _____Your, it's_____

4. (Your/You're) coat is much warmer than mine. _____Your_____

5. A whale needs air to breath. (It's/Its) blowhole is similar to our nose.
   _____Its_____

6. (Your/You're) very smart. _____You're_____

Fill in the sentence with the correct word.

7. _____We'd_____ like to go swimming. (We'd, Weed)

8. Michael is over _____there_____. (their, there)

9. _____It's_____ her first trip to Africa. (Its, It's)

10. Is that _____your_____ bike on the railing? (your, you're)

© Macmillan/McGraw-Hill

Vocabulary: Dictionary/Connotation and Denotation
- The **denotation** of a word tells what the word means.
- A word's **connotations** are the other words you think about with that word.
- For example, the denotation of the word *chair* might be *a place to sit*. The connotations for the word *chair* might be *a comfortable place to sit*.

Match the vocabulary word to its connotation. Use a dictionary to help you.

1. ___c___ invited   **a.** a planned activity

2. ___a___ program   **b.** annoy

3. ___d___ trusted   **c.** welcomed

4. ___b___ worry   **d.** counted on

Match the vocabulary word to its denotation. Use a dictionary to help you.

5. ___b___ announced   **a.** difficult to understand

6. ___d___ articles   **b.** made known

7. ___a___ complicated   **c.** made a great effort

8. ___c___ struggled   **d.** pieces of writing

Write two sentences using the words from the exercise.

Answers will vary.

9. _____

10. _____

Name _____

Phonics: Words with a VC/CV Pattern

Say the words below. Write 1 if the word has one syllable. Write 2 if the word has two syllables and draw a line between the syllables.

1. horse ___1___   2. robber ___2___

3. plain ___1___   4. most ___1___

5. bet|ter ___2___   6. kittens ___2___

7. spent ___1___   8. hurry ___1___

9. lad|der ___2___   10. hype ___1___

11. glow ___1___   12. funny ___2___

13. all ___1___   14. hap|pen ___2___

15. follow ___2___   16. day ___1___

Write four sentences with the words *better, hurry, funny,* and *follow*.

Answers will vary.

16. _____

17. _____

18. _____

19. _____

Comprehension: Summarize

Answer the questions below about *The ABC Volunteer*.

1. What did Jenny do every day after school?

   She went to the after-school program until evening.

2. Why did Jenny need to go to the after-school program?

   Her parents had to work, and didn't want her to stay home alone.

3. How did she feel when she met her student?

   She was nervous because he was an adult.

4. What did Jenny do as a volunteer?

   She taught Roberto how to read in English.

5. Why had Roberto not learned to read?

   He had to help his parents work in the fields when he was young.

6. Write a sentence about how Jenny felt in the beginning of the story.

   She felt bored and anxious.

7. Write a sentence about how Jenny felt when she heard about Roberto's childhood.

   She realized she was lucky to be able to go to school

   instead of working.

Language Structure: Adjectives

Underline each adjective. Circle the noun it describes.

1. It was a beautiful (day).

2. (Jenny) was happy with the after-school program.

3. The (article) was long.

4. The letter was written on scented (paper).

5. The (computer) was blue and silver.

6. The (game) was fun.

7. Sandy writes short (poems).

8. Mario has old (coins).

9. Jay read a funny (book).

10. Kate drank the hot (soup).

11. The (weather) was warm yesterday.

12. The (blanket) smelled fresh.

Write two sentences describing your classroom.
Underline the adjectives and circle the nouns they describe in each sentence.

13. _____ Answers will vary. _____

14. _____

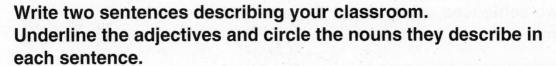

Name _____

Vocabulary: Thesaurus/Antonyms

• A word's **antonym** is a word that means the opposite of that word.

Circle the word in each row that is the antonym of the boldfaced word.

1. **play**	(work)	missing	funny
2. **bored**	tired	hurt	(interested)
3. **sick**	busy	(healthy)	awake
4. **cranky**	young	(cheerful)	bitter
5. **mean**	(polite)	sunny	come
6. **selfish**	absent	(thoughtful)	colorful
7. **sneaky**	(honest)	smelly	lazy
8. **tired**	late	gross	(energetic)

Write two sentences using two of the words above and their antonyms.

Answer will vary.

9. _____

10. _____

Name _____

Phonics: Words with V/CV and VC/V Patterns

Read each sentence aloud. Listen for the word with a long vowel
followed by consonant-vowel as in *music*. Circle the word.

1. I asked him for a (favor).

2. We will watch the (graceful) ballet tonight.

3. I will grow up to be (famous).

4. The (baby) fell asleep after she ate.

5. The audience was (silent) when Marta sang.

6. He told us he would be back in a (moment).

**Read each sentence aloud. Listen for the word with a short vowel
followed by consonant-vowel as in *taxi*. Circle the word.**

7. She has (talent).

8. Glen will (finish) the book tonight.

9. (Monarch) butterflies are pretty.

10. Zeke drank a cool glass of (water).

11. Steve saved his (money) to buy a new car.

12. We caught some fish in the (river).

Write two sentences using the words *famous* and *taxi*.

Answers will vary.

13. _____

14. _____

© Macmillan/McGraw-Hill

Name _____

Comprehension: Make Judgments

- A **judgment** is your opinion about a character, an action, or an idea in a book.

Use what you know and details from *Hans and Greta* to make a judgment. Write a judgment that tells your opinion about each detail.

1. Hans and Greta are going to Grandma Maggie's house.

   Judgment: Something interesting will happen at Grandma Maggie's house.

2. Greta plans to play tricks on Grandma's cat.

   Judgment: Greta likes to cause mischief.

3. Hans and Greta broke off part of Grandma's gingerbread house.

   Judgment: Hans and Greta might get in trouble.

4. Hans and Greta's stepmother told them not to play any tricks on Grandma Maggie.

   Judgment: Hans and Greta will play tricks anyway.

5. Greta decided to sneak up on the cat and scare it.

   Judgment: The cat gets scared and angry.

6. Hans and Greta promised not to play tricks on the cat while Grandma was away

   Judgment: The children learn their lesson about causing mischief.

Name _____

Language Structure: Articles

• The words *a, an,* and *the* are special adjectives called **articles**.

Underline the article or articles in each sentence.

1. Hans and Greta like to walk through the woods.

2. She makes a gingerbread house every year.

3. The children often help stir the cake batter.

4. John wants to be an actor.

5. The cat is sleeping by the fire.

Write three sentences using articles. Circle the articles.

Answers will vary.

6. _____

7. _____

8. _____

Name _____

Vocabulary: Analogies/Word Relationships

- An **analogy** shows how words are alike or different.
- For example, *hand* is to *glove* as *foot* is to *shoe*.

Hand   *is to*   **glove**   *as*   **foot**   *is to*   **shoe**

Complete each analogy with a word from the list.

deep	skeleton	float

1. Piece is to puzzle as bones are to _____. skeleton

2. Hold is to drop as sink is to _____. float

3. Sunny is to cloudy as shallow is to _____. deep

attract	puddles	environment

4. Fish is to ocean as animal is to _____. environment

5. Leave is to arrive as repel is to _____. attract

6. Mountain is to anthill as oceans are to _____. puddles

Write a sentence using one of the words in the box and its analogy

7. _____ Answers will vary.

Name _____

Phonics: Accented Syllables

Say each word aloud and listen for the syllable that has more stress. Circle the word that has more stress on the first syllable, as in *frosty* and *shower*.

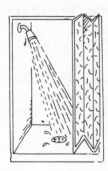

1. (button)   live   fish

2. balloon   gorilla   (silver)

3. sink   breath   (chamber)

4. chain   (diver)   salt

5. Spain   ray   (coral)

Complete the sentence below using one of the words you circled above.

6. The _____ saw many kinds of fish in the water.

7. Tropical fish can be white, black, _____, and all the colors of the rainbow.

8. The water is colder at the _____ of the ocean.

Comprehension: Fact and Opinion

- A **fact** is a statement that can be proven true.
- An **opinion** is a statement that cannot be proven, but can be supported or explained.

Read each sentence. Write fact or opinion.

opinion **1.** Fish are smelly, but they taste good if you grill them.

fact **2.** Some fish live in fresh water, and some live in salt water.

fact **3.** Fish breathe using gills.

opinion **4.** It is easier and more fun to swim in salt water.

fact **5.** Most of Earth's surface is covered with water.

opinion **6.** They should change the name of the Dead Sea because some tiny creatures do live there.

opinion **7.** It would be a lot of fun to go snorkeling and see fish in their natural environment.

fact **8.** Tropical fish come in many different colors and patterns.

Choose two opinions listed above. Write a different opinion for each.

Answers will vary.

9. _____

10. _____

Name _____

Language Structure: Adjectives that Compare

• **Adjectives** can be used to compare things.
  Underline the adjective in parentheses that best completes each sentence.

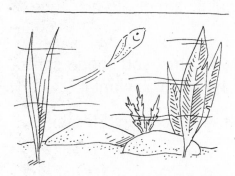

1. The Pacific Ocean is (colder / coldest) than the Atlantic Ocean.

2. The Dead Sea is the (saltier / saltiest) sea in the world.

3. Fish are one of the (older / oldest) creatures on Earth.

4. Bone is (harder / hardest) than cartilage.

5. It is (easier / easiest) to swim in fresh water.

6. The scientist reads the (later / latest) information.

Write four sentences. Use adjectives that compare in each.

Answers will vary.

7. _____

8. _____

9. _____

10. _____

Vocabulary: Context Clues/Descriptions
Read the sentences to find the meanings of the underlined words.

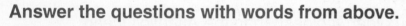

Some <u>artists</u> work with paint, some with clay, and some with stone.

When you move to a neew home, you spend some time <u>arranging</u> furniture the way you want it.

Diane's mother helped sew her <u>costume</u> for the school play.

Answer the questions with words from above.

1. Which word means *moving things around until you are happy*?   arranging

2. Which word means an *outfit for a performance*?   costume

3. Which word means people who are skilled in fine arts?   artists

Read the sentences to find the meanings of the underlined words.

Jin decided to walk to school to save on <u>expenses</u> instead of taking a cab.

Minnie was nervous about eating out with her parents at a <u>fancy</u> restaurant.

The lion at the zoo <u>flicked</u> his tail to shoo away some flies.

Answer the questions with words from above.

4. Which word means *quickly moved*?   flicked

5. Which word means *things you must pay for*?   expenses

6. Which word means *elegant,* or *lavish*?   fancy

© Macmillan/McGraw-Hill

Name _____

Phonics: Schwa + *r*

Read each word aloud. Listen to the *schwa + r* sound in *baker* and *maker.* Circle the word in each group with the *schwa + r* sound.

baker

1. door   (early)   sound

2. (doctor)   find   drive

3. time   dine   (singer)

4. please   (dinner)   where

5. act   hair   (her)

6. (litter)   paint   crowd

Write two sentences using the words *computer* and *finger*.

7. _____ Answers will vary. _____

8. _____

Write a word with the *schwa + r* sound.

9. _____ Answers will vary. _____

Comprehension: Character
Circle the letter that explains the characters' words or actions.

1. Louise is very surprised to hear that Madame Cassatt wants to paint a picture of her.

   a. She does not think she is as beautiful as the women she'd seen in paintings.

   b. She had better things to do like play outside.

2. Louise wanted to use the money she earned for voice lessons.

   a. Her parents wanted to add a swimming pool to their backyard.

   b. Her family's bakery provided for their needs, but not many luxuries.

3. Louise's sisters talked about what Madame Cassatt would have Louise wear.

   a. They were excited for her, and enjoyed picturing her dressed in fancy clothes.

   b. They were jealous, and wanted to embarrass Louise.

4. Louise was nervous when she went to Madame Cassatt's studio.

   a. She was not sure what to expect, or what the studio would look like.

   b. She heard that the studio was haunted by ghosts and monsters.

5. It was hard for Louise to sit still while her picture was being painted.

   a. She wanted to go swim in the pond near her house.

   b. Her arms were tired, and she found out that sitting so still was hard work.

Language Structure: Comparing with *More* and *Most*

- Add **more** or **most** to adjectives with two or more syllables. When you use **more** or **most**, do not use the *-er* or *-est* form of an adjective.

Complete the sentences below with *more* or *most*.

1. It was the ___most___ beautiful painting I'd ever seen.

2. Sheila was ___more___ professional than Tammy.

3. That was the ___most___ glorious piece of jewelry in the shop.

4. Carl's pictures were ___more___ colorful than before.

5. The painting was ___more___ interesting than the sculpture.

6. Tammy painted the ___most___ complicated scene.

Write two sentences. In the first sentence compare with *more* and an adjective. In the second sentence compare with *most* and an adjective.

Answers will vary.

7. _____

8. _____

Vocabulary: Context Clues/Paragraph Clues

• Other words in a sentence can help you learn the meaning of a word you do not know. These words are called **context clues.**

Read the paragraphs below. Notice the underlined words. Write the context clues that help you figure out the meaning of the underlined words.

Grandpa keeps many <u>horses</u> in his barn. They are very good animals. They run very fast and help him watch his sheep. He likes to <u>ride</u> them on the <u>plains</u>. They carry him across the huge, grassy land. When I visit, he likes to teach me how to take care of them. Pretty soon, I will be able to ride them too!

1. horses _____ very good animals, run very fast _____

2. ride _____ they carry him _____

3. plains _____ huge, grassy land _____

The Native Americans learned to survive on the Great Plains. They used horses to carry their <u>supplies</u>, or things they needed. The Native Americans had to protect themselves against <u>enemies</u>, or people from other tribes who could harm or steal from them. They made <u>weapons</u>, or tools they could use to defend themselves. They made sharp spears from the bones of buffalo.

4. supplies _____ things they needed _____

5. enemies _____ people who could harm or steal from them _____

6. weapons _____ tools they could use to defend themselves _____

Name _____

Phonics: Schwa + *l*

Read each word aloud. Listen for the *schwa + l* sound as in *tumble* and *camel*. Circle the word in each group that has the *schwa + l* sound.

camel

tumble

1. sun   (saddle)   slide

2. (animal)   call   horse

3. four   fall   (fragile)

4. ball   (battle)   half

5. (triangle)   bill   brilliant

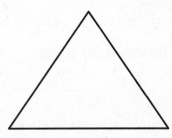

Think of three more words with the *schwa + l* sound. Write them on the lines below.

Answers will vary.

6. _____

7. _____

8. _____

© Macmillan/McGraw-Hill

Name _____

Comprehension: Cause and Effect
- A **cause** is why something happens.
- An **effect** is what happened.

Read each cause. Then write the effect that occurred because of it.

Example:

Cause: Native Americans who lived on the Great Plains needed to hunt buffalo for food.

Effect: __**They became good hunters.**__

1. Cause: Buffalo could smell the hunters coming, and run away.

   Effect: The hunters covered themselves with wolf skins to trick the buffalo.

2. Cause: Native Americans needed clothes, tools, meat, and other items.

   Effect: They learned how to use every part of the buffalo for their needs.

3. Cause: Native Americans needed to be able to hunt the buffalo even when the herd had traveled far away.

   Effect: They used horses so that they could go on longer hunting trips.

4. Cause: Hunters on horseback need to steer the horse while using their hands to hunt.

   Effect: They taught their horses to respond to signals they gave with their knees.

5. Cause: Many tribes wanted to hunt on the same land.

   Effect: Sometimes there were wars between tribes.

Comprehension: Cause and Effect

- A **cause** is why something happened.
- An **effect** is what happened.

Match each cause to its effect.

Causes

1. __d__ People wanted land of their own to farm or raise cattle.

2. __a__ The idea of finding gold was very exciting to many people.

3. __f__ Settlers wanted the land in Georgia, where the Cherokee people were living.

4. __e__ Russian miners discovered gold in Alaska, above Canada.

5. __g__ Prospecting for gold in the snow was dangerous because miners could get hurt.

6. __b__ Settlers and miners needed a way to get supplies.

7. __c__ There were no towns in Pike's Peak before the gold rush.

Effects

a. Many people rushed to where gold had been found. They hoped to find some too.

b. Workers built roads and railroads so supplies could reach the mines.

c. Prospectors built boomtowns in Pike's Peak.

d. People traveled west to find land they could farm.

e. Prospectors went north through Canada to look for gold in Alaska.

f. The Army forced the Cherokee off of their own land. The Army made them move to Oklahoma.

g. Miners strapped spikes called creepers to their boots to keep them from slipping on ice.

© Macmillan/McGraw-Hill

Name _____

Language Structure: Comparing with *Good* and *Bad*

- *Good* and *bad* have special forms when used for **comparing**.

Underline the word in parentheses that best completes each sentence.

1. I like the summer (good, better, best).

2. We watched a (bad, worse, worst) movie.

3. Carrie is a (good, better, best) judge of character.

4. That was the (bad, worse, worst) hamburger I have ever eaten.

5. Pintos are (good, better, best) at jumping than other breeds of horses.

6. Dogs are (good, better, best) pets.

7. Cowboys are (good, better, best) horse riders.

8. The weather was (bad, worse, worst).

Write a sentence with the word *worse*.

9. _____ Answers will vary. _____

Write a sentence with the word *better*.

10. _____ Answers will vary. _____

© Macmillan/McGraw-Hill

Name _____

Vocabulary: Word Parts/Suffixes

• A **suffix** is a word ending that changes a word's meaning.

Use what you have learned about suffixes to answer the questions. Check your answers in the dictionary.

Example: **Inventing** means to create something new and useful.

1. What does an **inventor** do?

An inventor is someone who creates something new and useful.

2. Farming is growing food for people to eat. What does a **farmer** do?

A farmer is someone who grows food for people to eat.

3. Working means doing a job or a task that needs to be done. What does a **worker** do?

A worker does a job or task that needs to be done.

4. To **supply** someone means to bring things for him or her to sell or use. What does a **supplier** do?

A supplier brings things for someone to sell or use.

5. Inspecting means making sure something is real or safe. What does an **inspector** do?

An inspector meakes sure something is real or safe.

6. Camping means sleeping outside in a tent while enjoying nature. What does a **camper** do?

A camper sleeps outside a tent while enjoying nature.

Name _____

Phonics: Schwa + *n*

Read each word aloud. Circle the word with a schwa + *n* th has the same sound as the underlined letters in *hum<u>an</u>*.

human   **cabin**   **garden**   **butt**

1. We ___listen___ to the radio in the car.

people   listen   ten

2. People traveled by covered ___wagon___ in the 1800s.

wagon   walk   own

3. There were ___seven___ cookies left in the jar.

journey   tears   seven

4. I ___often___ ride my bike to school.

often   always   sometimes

5. A ___woman___ lived in an old town of the West.

been   woman   man

Write a sentence using a word with the *schwa + n* sound.

6. ___Answers will vary.___ _____

Name _____

Language Structure: Adverbs

- An **adverb** describes a verb. Adverbs can tell how, when, or where an action takes place.

Underline the adverb in each sentence. Then write if the adverb tells *how, when,* or *where*.

1. The gold glinted brightly in those hills. _____how_____

2. Gold prospectors often had disappointments. _____when_____

3. The Cherokee had to travel far to get to their new home. _____where_____

4. Boomtowns in the West grew quickly. _____how_____

5. The gold prospector looked around for gold. _____where_____

6. Many prospectors were soon annoyed that they could not find gold. _____when_____

Write three sentences using adverbs. Circle the adverbs.

Answers will vary.

7. _____

8. _____

9. _____

Name _____

Vocabulary: Context Clues/Paragraph Clues
Read the sentences. Put them in order to make a paragraph.

1. Trying to be very brave, I climbed the tree.

2. I knew I had to rescue her, but I was scared to climb so high.

3. Patches jumped on my shoulder and let me carry her down.

4. My cat Patches climbed a tree and got stuck.

My cat, Patches, climbed a tree and got stuck. I knew I had to rescue her, but I was scared to climb so high. Trying to be very brave, I climbed the tree. Patches jumped on my shoulder and let me carry her down.

Read the sentences. Put them in order to make a paragraph.

5. It was like the whole city was a big playground!

6. The best part was when I held onto the edge of a tall building and tried to slide down the side like a pole.

7. I was so big that I had to bend over not to hit the ceiling.

8. I had a dream that I was bigger than any other human I'd ever seen.

I had a dream that I was bigger than any other human I'd ever seen. I was so big that I had to bend over not to hit the ceiling. The best part was when I held onto the edge of a tall building and tried to slide down the side like a pole. It was like the whole city was a big playground!

Name _____

Phonics: Homophones

- **Homophones** are words that sound the same, but have different meanings.

The <u>pair</u> of girls stood on the playground. They each had a <u>pear</u> with their lunches.

Circle the words in each group that are homophones.

1. (two)   (too)   top

2. bent   (scents)   (cents)

3. (fair)   fake   (fare)

4. (where)   (ware)   (wear)

5. hose   (flew)   (flu)

Write sentences using four homophones from above.

6. _____

7. _____

8. _____

9. _____

© Macmillan/McGraw-Hill

Comprehension: Theme

• A **theme** is the main idea in a piece of writing.

Answer the questions about *In the Land of the Giants*. Then, choose the theme that fits the story best.

1. What did Roberto see when he woke up?

He saw mice on his pillow.

2. What did they want Roberto to do?

They wanted him to rescue a dog named the Sad One.

3. How did Roberto get to the land of the giants?

He climbed a very tall tree.

4. How did Roberto feel when he went into the land of the giants?

He was scared to be up so high, and that he might get stepped on.

5. Which theme is logical for the story so far?

   a. Traveling to new places

   b. How to care for pets

   c. Being brave when you need to

6. What is one problem Roberto had in the land of the giants?

Possible answers: being so small, having to climb up to the dog's

cage, staying away from the giants.

Name _____

Language Structure: Comparing with Adverbs

- Add **-er** to an adverb to compare two actions.
- Add **-est** to compare more than two actions.

Circle the correct adverb to complete each sentence.

Example: The dog has a (cleaner, cleanest) cage that the hamsters.

1. Robert woke up (earlier, earliest) than he had planned.

2. The oak tree was the (taller, tallest) in the park.

3. Sally ran (faster, fastest) than Margaret.

4. The giant lived in the (bigger, biggest) house Jack had ever seen.

5. Ken's room was (neat, neater) than his brother's room.

Write two sentences using adverbs that compare.

Answers will vary.

6. _____

7. _____

© Macmillan/McGraw-Hill

Name _____

Vocabulary: Word Parts/Latin Roots

- Some words in English come from the **Latin** language.

noct = night	audi = to hear	fort = luck, chance
vulcanus = a God of fire		rupt = to break out

Read the sentences below. Then write the Latin root from the word box for each underlined word.

1. ____erupt____ Many people died when Mount Vesuvius <u>erupted</u>.

2. ____vulcanus____ When the <u>volcano</u> erupted, lava flowed down the hillside.

3. ____audi____ Jodi was excited to hear her favorite pianist play in her school <u>auditorium</u>.

4. ____noct____ <u>Nocturnal</u> animals, such as owls, stay awake at night.

5. ____fort____ We are <u>fortunate</u> to be able to visit the city of Pompeii.

Write two sentences using two of the underlined words from above.

6. _____Answers will vary._____

7. _____

Name _____

Phonics: Words with Prefixes *dis-*, *mis-*, *non-*, and *un-*

Match each prefix to a word on the right. Write the new word.

1. _____discover_____ dis-   **a.** wrap

2. _____mislead_____ mis-   **b.** fat

3. _____nonfat_____ non-   **c.** lead

4. _____unwrap_____ un-   **d.** cover

Match each prefix to a word on the right. Write the new word.

5. _____discontinue_____ dis-   **a.** fair

6. _____misunderstand_____ mis-   **b.** sense

7. _____nonsense_____ non-   **c.** understand

8. _____unfair_____ un-   **d.** continue

Write a sentence using a new word from above.

9. ___Possible answer: Boris thought he got an unfair___

___score on his performance.___

Name _____

Comprehension: Make Generalizations

- A **generalization** is a statement that tells about groups of people or things.
- A **generalization** usually has clue words like these: *most, always, never,* and *all*.

Read each sentence. Write the clue word that shows you it is a generalization.

1. Most of the people in Pompeii died when Vesuvius erupted.

   Clue word: _____most_____

2. The people always liked to visit the town center, or forum.

   Clue word: _____always_____

3. All of the homes were destroyed by lava.

   Clue word: _____all_____

4. Never before had people seen such a disaster on their island.

   Clue word: _____never_____

5. All of the people heard the volcano erupt.

   Clue word: _____all_____

6. Many people thought they would be safe in their homes.

   Clue word: _____many_____

7. Most of the ships in the harbor were destroyed by large waves.

   Clue word: _____most_____

8. Nobody ever thought a whole city was under all of the ashes.

   Clue word: _____ever_____

Language Structure: Negatives

- A **negative** is a word that means "no." Some negatives include the contraction *n't*. Never use two negatives in one sentence.

Circle the negative in each sentence

1. (Nobody) expected to find Pompeii.

2. The people of Pompeii (didn't) know that the volcano was about to erupt.

3. The art and treasures were (not) protected.

4. (No) one survived the eruption.

The sentence below is false. Make the sentence true by using the negative.

Pompeii was a city near Mount Etna.

5. _Pompeii was not a city near Mount Etna. It was a city near Mount Vesuvius._

Vocabulary: Word Parts/Inflectional Endings

Add -ed and -ing to these words to create new words.

	- ed	- ing
1. crash	crashed	crashing
2. land	landed	landing
3. watch	watched	watching
4. turn	turned	turning
5. excite	excited	exciting
6. expect	expected	expecting
7. lift	lifted	lifting
8. steer	steered	steering

Write a sentence using one of the words with an inflectional ending above.

Example: The boat almost crashed into a bridge.

9. _____ Answers will vary. _____

10. _____

Phonics: Words with Suffixes -*y*, -*ly*, -*ful*, -*less*, -*ness*

Add the suffixes -*y*, -*ly*, -*ful*, -*less*, and -*ness* to the words below to create new words. Write the new word on the line.

Name _____

1. sunn + y   _____sunny_____

2. week + ly   _____weekly_____

3. joy + ful   _____joyful_____

4. fear + less   _____fearless_____

5. dark + ness   _____darkness_____

6. worth + y   _____worthy_____

7. clear + ly   _____clearly_____

Choose three new words from above. Write a sentence using each.

Answers will vary.

8. _____

9. _____

10. _____

Name _____

Comprehension: Author's Perspective

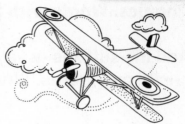

- The **author's perspective is** how the author thinks or feels about a topic.

Read the details from *Riding the Wind: Amelia Earhart.* Match the detail with the author's perspective.

Details	Author's Perspective
1. __f__ Women were not expected to be pilots. They were expected to stay home as wives and mothers.	**a.** The author thinks that Lindbergh's flight made Amelia want to try too.
2. __c__ Amelia's family attended an air show. They watched the pilots do tricks.	**b.** The author believes Amelia should have been allowed to help fly the plane across the ocean.
3. __d__ Amelia painted her first plane yellow and called it the *Canary.*	**c.** The author thinks watching the air show made Amelia want to fly.
4. __e__ Amelia pretended to go on many adventures when she was a little girl.	**d.** The author thinks Amelia liked feeling like a bird when she flew.
5. __a__ Charles Lindbergh flew across the Atlantic Ocean in 1927.	**e.** The author thinks Amelia was always a brave and adventurous person.
6. __b__ When Amelia flew across the Atlantic Ocean the first time, she was not allowed to do the flying.	**f.** The author believes it was not fair that women were not allowed to be pilots.

Name _____

Language Structure: Prepositions and Prepositional Phrases

- A **preposition** is a group of words that begins with a preposition and ends with a noun or pronoun.

Circle the preposition. Underline the noun or pronoun that follows it.

1. Joan was hoisted (onto) the plane.

2. Elena often rides (on) airplanes.

3. Amelia got her pilot license (after) she moved (to) California.

4. John is a pilot (for) an airline.

Write two sentences describing the pictures above. Be sure to use prepositions. Circle the preposition

5. _Possible answer: The bird is standing (on) the box._

6. _Possible answer: The cat is sitting (in) the basket._

Name _____

Vocabulary: Word Parts/Greek Roots

• Some words in English come from the Greek language.

**Read the definitions of the Greek roots. Match
the Greek root and the English word.**

geo = earth	zo = animal	crit = judge
astr = star	derm = skin	phyll = leaf

1. __b__ geo   **a.** criticize

2. __c__ zo   **b.** geology

3. __a__ crit   **c.** zoo

4. __d__ astr   **d.** astronomy

5. __e__ derm   **e.** dermatology

6. __f__ phyll   **f.** chlorophyll

**Look up two of the English words above in the dictionary. Write
its definition.**

7. Word: _Possible answer: geology_

   Definition: _study of the earth_

8. Word: _Possible answer: criticize_

   Definition: _to judge what is good or bad about_

   something or someone

Phonics: Words with Stressed Syllables

Read aloud the words below. Circle the word in each group with the *-er* sound as in *stir* and *Earth*.

1. her   moth   except

2. iris   early   error

3. eggs   sir   head

4. small   knob   earn

5. infer   fly   wing

6. leg   earnest   monarch

7. bark   read   blur

8. grand   were   core

9. transfer   write   tire

Choose two words from above. Write a sentence using each.

Answers will vary.

10. _____

11. _____

© Macmillan/McGraw-Hill

Name _____

Comprehension: Description

• An author uses **description** to explain
the qualities or characteristics of something.

**Write a description from _Butterflies and Moths_
for the topics below.**

1. Describe how many kinds of moths and butterflies there are in the
world.

    There are more than 20,000 kinds of butterflies,

    and 250,000 kinds of moths.

2. Describe what butterflies and moths do to help nature.

    They take pollen from flower to flower and are

    food for other animals.

3. Describe a butterfly's body.

    They have three body parts.

4. Describe a butterfly's wings.

    They are colorful, strong, and light.

5. Describe what happens to caterpillars.

    They make a cocoon and stay in it until they are

    ready to become butterflies.

6. Describe how moths and butterflies avoid being eaten.

    They have colors and patterns that help them

    hide among plants.

Name _____

Language Structure: Sentences with Prepositions

• Two sentences can be combined by adding a **prepositional phrase** to one sentence.

Underline the prepositional phrase in the second sentence. Then, combine the sentences by adding a prepositional phrase to the first sentence.

1. Butterflies and moths take pollen. They take pollen from flower to flower.

   Butterflies and moths take pollen from flower to flower.

2. Suddenly, the butterfly flew. It flew onto the opposite tree.

   Suddenly, the butterfly flew onto the opposite tree.

3. Adult moths and butterflies sip nectar. They sip nectar from flowers.

   Adult moths and butterflies sip nectar from flowers.

4. Monarch butterflies fly south. They fly south in the winter.

   Monarch butterflies fly south in the winter.

Write a sentence using a prepositional phrase.

5. _____ Answers will vary. _____

Vocabulary Tic Tac Toe

Materials

- Chalkboard
- Chalk
- Students' vocabulary cards

- On the board, draw a large grid with nine squares.
- Have students take out their vocabulary cards for the unit. Ask students to choose nine vocabulary words and tell you what they are. Write each of the words they choose in each of the nine squares.
- Have students work in two teams: Team X and Team O. The X team chooses a word and tries to use it correctly in an oral sentence. If they use the word correctly, erase the word and draw an X in the square that the team chooses.
- Teams take turns repeating the activity until one team has a three X's or three O's in a row.
- Repeat the activity with nine more vocabulary words.

Snakey Board Game

Materials

- Butcher paper
- Marker
- Games pieces
- Removable tape
- Number cube
- Students' vocabulary cards

- On a length of butcher paper, draw a large snake and divide it into 20 squares. Write START in the first square and END in the last square.
- Have students take out their vocabulary cards from the unit. Let them choose 10 words and tape one word to each of the 10 random squares. In other squares, write directions, such as *Go Back 1 Square* or *Move Ahead 2 Squares*.
- Read aloud all the words and directions.
- Invite groups of four children to take turns playing the game. Have the first child roll the number cube and move his or her game piece the same number of squares. The child will read aloud the vocabulary word on that square and define the word through role play or simple language. If the child correctly uses the word, he or she may remain on the square. If not, the child must return to START.
- Play continues until the first child reaches END.

Two by Two

- Have students create two teams which will form two lines. Call one line *Team A* and the other line *Team B*. Students will compete in pairs.
- Show a vocabulary card from the unit to the first student in each line. The first student to correctly read the card has the chance to then define the word. If the student can do both tasks correctly, he or she scores a point for their team. Both students then go to the back of the line and the game continues with the next pair of students.
- If both students read the word correctly at the same time, show them a different card until one student reads it before the other student.

Riddle Posters

Materials

- Posterboard
- Marker
- Students' vocabulary cards
- Two rolls of removable tape

- Write 18 riddles that can be answered with vocabulary words from the unit.
- On each of two large pieces of posterboard, draw nine squares. In each square, write one of the riddles.
- Have students take out their vocabulary cards for the unit.
- Have students work in two groups. Give each group a roll of tape and one poster. Have each group work together to choose the word that is the answer to a riddle, and place that word where it belongs in each box.
- Divide children into two groups. Provide each group with a roll of tape and one poster. Have each group work together to choose the word that is the answer to a riddle, and place that word where it belongs in each box.
- When a group finishes placing all the correct answers on the poster, the game is over. Students can check each other's work by reading aloud the riddles and answers.

What's My Word?

Materials

- Chalkboard
- Chalk
- Students' vocabulary cards

- Tell students to take out their vocabulary cards
- Have students work in two teams. Line up the teams, so that students can take turns when it is that team's turn to go to the board.
- The first team chooses a word from their word cards and a student from that team writes it on the board. The first person in line on the other team must correctly use the word in a sentence. If the student does this, their team gets a point. If the student cannot do this, they give the question back to the first team, who gets a point if their student can make a sentence with the word. The first team to earn 10 points wins the game.

Sentence Mix-Up

Materials

- Strips of paper
- Marker
- Scissors
- Paper clips

- Prepare sentences with vocabulary words from the unit on strips of paper. Then cut each sentence apart so that all the words are separate. Take out the pieces that have the vocabulary words. Mix up the remaining words that make up each sentence, and paper clip the words for each sentence together.
- Have students take out their vocabulary cards for the unit.
- Have the class work in small groups. Give each group one paper-clipped group of words. Have groups race to put each clipped group of words together with one of their vocabulary words, in an order that makes a correct sentence. Then have them write the sentence on the board. The first team to do so wins.

Beginning

ad	clues
evidence	mystery
solve	surprise

© Macmillan/McGraw-Hill

Intermediate

clues	creativity
evidence	owner
planned	records
stealing	suspicious

Advanced

accuse	allergies
assignments	consideration
consume	evidence
suspicious	

Beginning

adaptations

climate

cool

desert

survive

Intermediate

adaptations	**behaviors**
climate	**escape**
scarce	**swallows**
temperature	

Advanced

climate	eerie
lumbering	lurk
shimmer	silken
swallows	

Beginning

hunt	island
national park	protect
wildlife	

Intermediate

dams	marshes
pond	protect
tadpoles	waterfalls
wildlife	

Advanced

completed

journey

natural

roamed

wildlife

Beginning

apartment

elevator

intruder

strange

trouble

Intermediate

astronauts	**cool**
guards	**intruder**
machines	**top secret**
trouble	**uniforms**

Name _____

Advanced

astronauts	endless
paralyzed	protested
realistic	sensible
universe	

Beginning

ambulance	bandage
bite	code
rattlesnake	secret

The Secret Code • **Unit 1 Week 5**

Name _____

Intermediate

code	hug
raft	rattlesnake
scout	slithered

Advanced

cluttered	disgusted
downstream	nuzzle
raft	scattered

Advanced

flinched

fluke

gaped

insult

legendary

muttered

snickering

Beginning

boycotts	**grapes**
kitchen	**owners**
restaurant	**shopping**

Intermediate

boycotts	**business**
chef	**convince**
customers	**grocery**
opportunities	**owners**

border

boycotts

citizen

opportunities

overheard

strikes

unions

Name _____

Beginning

bamboo	**cub**
danger	**forests**
panda	

Intermediate

cub

danger

habitat

hollow

preserve

regions

separate

treasures

Advanced

dynasties

heritage

overjoyed

preserve

temples

Beginning

battlefield	**Civil War**
hospitals	**nursed**
soldiers	**wounded**

Intermediate

battlefield	**caring**
came in handy	**disasters**
emergencies	**independence**
officials	**treatment**

Advanced

convinced	dizzy
came in handy	hilarious
independence	mischief
nowadays	whirlwind

Beginning

marshes	**molt**
poison	**rain forest**
slither	**tongue**

Intermediate

creatures	dangerous
harmless	inject
molt	predators
swamps	threatened

Name _____

Advanced

ambulance

apologize

cardboard

genuine

harmless

slithered

weekdays

Beginning

frighten	monster
scarecrow	scary
tricked	woods

Intermediate

budge	**frighten**
guardian	**mischief**
peaceful	**tricked**
tugged	

Advanced

agile	awkward
guardian	interfere
proclaimed	tottered

Beginning

captives

escaped

freedom

guided

slavery

Intermediate

auction	capture
crossed	freedom
runaways	segregation
slavery	unfair

Advanced

ancestors	**avoided**
injustice	**numerous**
segregation	**unfair**
unsuspecting	

Beginning

inventors	raised
stand for	system
young	

Name _____

Intermediate

arranging	enterprising
interested	legal document
published	raised
receive	stand for

© Macmillan/McGraw-Hill

Advanced

enterprising

identified

persistence

venture

Beginning

drowned

dunes

legend

reached

shore

Intermediate

amazement	den
floated	reached
roaring	shore
surface	upset

Name _____

Advanced

amazement

loosened

midst

mysterious

patchwork

responsibility

sores

Beginning

hurricanes

damage

hit

humid

speed

storm

Intermediate

damage	evaporates
floods	hit
measure	property
season	shelter

Advanced

blizzard	evaporate
foolishness	inspire
magnify	microscope
negatives	technique

Name _____

Beginning

actors

commands

starred

talented

trainer

tricks

Intermediate

adventure	**commands**
filmmakers	**misunderstood**
perform	**signals**
skills	**starred**

Name _____

Advanced

appreciated	bluffing
desperate	endured
misunderstood	neglected
obedience	risks

Beginning

accomplishments	**blood**
discovered	**donate**
lose	**store**

Name ____________________

Vocabulary Cards

Intermediate

accomplishments	bleeding
donate	graduated
infections	message
organize	spoil

Advanced

cautiously	**crisscrossed**
disguised	**fade**
faint	**jealous**
wisdom	

Beginning

ability	battery
dams	energy
heat	source

Intermediate

ability	ancient
burned	decayed
fuels	proved
run out	source

Advanced

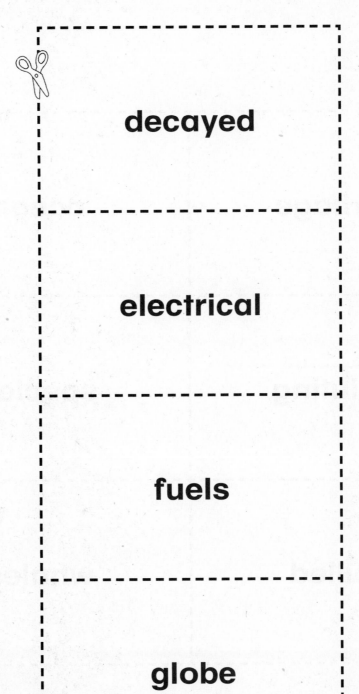

decayed

electrical

fuels

globe

Beginning

garbage	ocean
polluting	species
spilled	whales

Intermediate

bay

dove

dump

feed

food chain

journey

species

tame

© Macmillan/McGraw-Hill

Advanced

dove	**massive**
politicians	**rumbling**
snoring	**tangles**
unique	

© Macmillan/McGraw-Hill

Beginning

creatures

explorer

food chain

frozen

sleds

surface

Intermediate

brittle	crack
deep	defense
explorer	party
passage	tough

Advanced

brittle

coral

current

eventually

partnership

reef

suburbs

Beginning

gift	invited
program	public library
trusted	volunteer

Intermediate

announced	articles
complicated	crops
gift	peculiar
struggled	teenage

Advanced

advanced	consisted
peculiar	positive
selecting	snuffled

Name _____

Beginning

flour	gingerbread
oven	play tricks
promise	stepmother

Intermediate

cranky	flour
mean	ruined
selfish	sneaks up
stepmother	tired

© Macmillan/McGraw-Hill

Advanced

bumbling	commotion
cranky	exasperated
famished	selfish
specialty	

Name _____

Beginning

bony	**crafts**
deep	**float**
gills	**skeleton**

Intermediate

attract	body of water
environment	fins
float	patterns
puddles	vessels

Advanced

documenting	estimated
period	valuable
vessels	

Beginning

artist	arranging
costume	interesting
model	painting

Intermediate

arranging	**costume**
expenses	**fancy**
flicked	**gallery**
jewelry	**twist**

Advanced

barbecue

collage

flicked

glorious

skyscraper

strutting

swarms

Beginning

decorate	horses
Plains	ride
symbols	tribes

Intermediate

enemies	experts
Plains	spears
strength	supplies
threatened	weapons

Advanced

coaxing	**descendants**
fragile	**glistening**
habitat	**sanctuary**
threatened	

Beginning

forced	gold rush
metal	settlers
starved	supplies

Intermediate

axes	campfire
prospectors	risk
settlers	spread
tracks	valuable

Name _____

Advanced

annoyed	circular
disappointment	glinted
outstretched	prospectors
reference	

Beginning

brave	climb
dreaming	giants
rescue	rope

Advanced

fossils	inspected
paleontologists	professionals
stumbled upon	

Beginning

crashed	**dangerous**
flight	**landed**
pilots	**set a record**

Name _____

Intermediate

crashed	**excited**
expected	**landed**
lent	**lifting**
steer a course	**stunts**

Advanced

| applauded | assured |

| glider | headlines |

| hoisting | unstable |

| wingspan | |

Name _____

Beginning

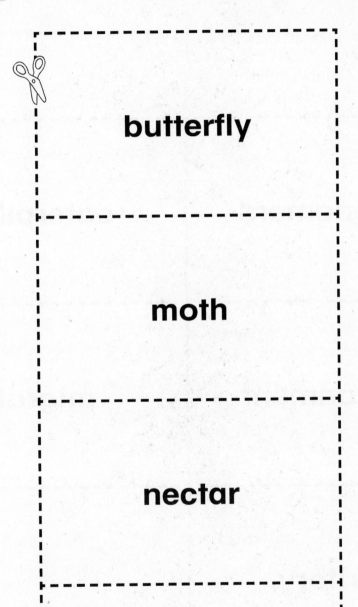

butterfly

moth

nectar

pollen

Intermediate

astronomers

caterpillar

environment

migrate

territory

Advanced

astronomer	communication
investigates	nutrients
overcome	prehistoric
solitary	territory